.

ROBERT ATKINSON
1883–1952

THE ARCHITECTURAL ASSOCIATION · LONDON · in collaboration with · THE BARBER INSTITUTE · UNIVERSITY OF BIRMINGHAM

ROBERT ATKINSON
1883–1952

CONTENTS

front cover:
entrance hall of the Daily Express Building,
London, 1932

*Amusement Park
and Trades Exhibition
Hall, Salford, 1927*

ROBERT ATKINSON 1883–1952

Gavin Stamp

If an artist is wise he expresses himself in a language sufficiently familiar and uses a vocabulary as rich and simple as possible... We shall always be liable to Gothic 'revival' while our cathedrals stand on our soil, we shall always be liable to Classic 'revival' while we fight against fog and have in our streets the least sunlight to remind us of Italy and Italian cities. But they are languages which cannot be constantly used with unchanged idiom in changed surroundings. We speak English today but we do not use the idiom of Chaucer. In our architectural languages we have to select and add, and admit new terms and expressions, yet all the while keep a clear grasp of the original structural and climatic meanings.[1]

Such was the view of architectural style expressed in 1926 by Robert Atkinson, by then Director of Education at the Architectural Association School, and his co-author, Hope Bagenal, Librarian at the AA, in the single published volume of their planned educational treatise on the *Theory and Elements of Architecture*. In his own work Atkinson never, in fact, expressed himself in Gothic but he used most other styles – American Beaux-Arts, neo-Grec, neo-Georgian, Arts and Crafts vernacular, Romanesque, American Art Deco, Modernistic and even Brighton Oriental. All were handled with intelligence, with tact and in a distinctive personal manner. But even in today's Post-Modern and eclectic architectural climate, such a catholic and undogmatic attitude to style is not fully understood and, in consequence, the architecture of Robert Atkinson is comparatively little known.

Reputations are fragile things. Because he had no distinctive personal style, or styles, as did his peers Edwin Lutyens and Giles Gilbert Scott, and because he did not embrace the Modern Movement, as did younger contemporaries like Oliver Hill

1 Robert Atkinson and Hope Bagenal, *Theory and Elements of Architecture*, vol.1, part 1, 1926, p.10.

5

and Joseph Emberton, Atkinson's work has been largely ignored in the modern literature about British architecture between the two world wars. Perhaps he is best known not for a building but for an interior – the entrance hall of the Daily Express Building in Fleet Street. Yet for Charles Reilly in 1929, writing the only profile of the architect to appear in his lifetime, there was:

> ... no one else in the architectural profession today in this country who has played so many parts, and who has done them all so well and is yet several years short of fifty years of age, like Robert Atkinson. Sitting down to collect one's ideas about him, one does not know where to begin. Which is the more important aspect of him: Atkinson the brilliant ornamentalist and colourist; Atkinson the vigorous architect and planner; Atkinson the real founder, organizer, and inspirer of our biggest School of Architecture; Atkinson the great draughtsman; or Atkinson the joint author of the best modern book on architectural theory? Surely no other young man of forty-six has such a record?[2]

Reilly's hero clearly deserves attention, both on his own account and because such a versatile career must surely illuminate the history of the times in which he lived. And these are difficult times to understand – once it is accepted that British architecture in the 1920s and 30s is much, much more than the triumph of the Modern Movement, that the period is as stylistically confused and eclectic, as divided and as vigorous as the mid Victorian decades. During these complex years, Atkinson belonged to the generation that was in the thick of things.

Generations were important. The older generation – Lutyens, Baker, Blomfield – was still active and creative in the 1920s, but the values it embraced and the traditions it maintained were essentially Edwardian, even Victorian. The younger generation, who trained in the 1920s, explored new solutions, new materials and new styles in the revolutionary climate engendered by the trauma of the First World War. To such men, rebelling against their parents' values, the past became an increasing irrelevance in a dynamic, progressive, technological age. Yet it was the generation in the middle, the one that survived the trenches, which often had the most mature, intelligent and civilized response to the challenges of the post-war decades.

Born in 1883, Atkinson was of this middle generation, (although he, unlike his partner Alexander, or his contemporary Charles Gascoyne, did not actually serve in the War). It was a generation deeply impressed by the modernity of America. Atkinson, like, say, Giles Gilbert Scott or H. S. Goodhart-Rendel, was far from being a simple traditionalist; he was open to new ideas but treated them with a degree of caution. He felt that historical styles must develop and that a modern idiom, suitable for the times, must emerge. It was clear to him that a degree of restraint, of simplicity and even austerity was demanded by the post-war climate. Like Scott, he rose to the challenge of new building types, trying his hand not only at large electric power stations but tackling also the complex problems presented by modern theatre and cinema design. Atkinson was a pioneer in cinema architecture and arguably the first top-rate architect seriously to involve himself in this new

2 C. H. Reilly, *Representative British Architects of the Present Day*, 1931, p.29, reprint of article which first appeared in *Building*.

6

field. It can also be claimed that he was the designer of the first steel-framed church in the country and of the first purpose-built institution for teaching art history.

But, like Scott again, he could only go so far down the road towards Modernism. He was a product of his time and, as a theatre designer, well knew the value of colour, ornament and decoration. He was not prepared to forget all the lessons of the past; he also knew the value of experience and of well-tried techniques and building materials:

> Architecture carries with it the labours and fatigues of an active historical process, in which the needs and ideas of men living and dead, the materials available, and the temper of workers, are stubborn factors... An architect who ignores what has been done in the past is in danger of wasting his time solving problems – structural and artistic – which have ben solved already. Great men have built before us – of the same physical stature as ourselves, as acute, and using the same crust of the earth for materials...[3]

Atkinson could not, therefore, accept the *tabula rasa* required by the 1930s Modern Movement, nor its utopianism, structural as well as social. Nor, apparently, was he prepared to handle Modernism as just one of several available styles, as could Oliver Hill. Atkinson's most truly 'Modern' scheme, demonstrating a sound grasp of Modern planning and structure, was his abortive project of 1934 for a hotel in Blackpool, while his project for Salford of 1927 envisaged a spectacular reinforced-concrete arched structure to be engineered by Owen Williams. However, both as a teacher and as an influential and established architect, he was very happy to encourage younger men to travel in the new direction. He was, significantly, on the building committee for Maxwell Fry's Kensal House; also, a newspaper interviewer reported in 1932 that, although Atkinson had 'a high standard of criticism and is rather severe on many present-day men', he was, nonetheless, 'optimistic concerning the younger men and believes that the Modern Movement is gaining strength... Modern architecture, he said, had involved a much closer drawing together of the architect and the engineer. The latter, however, must always remain strictly utilitarian, even though there were engineers who, on the strength of having designed a factory, were calling themselves architects.'[4] (Surely Atkinson could not have been thinking of Owen Williams, whose dramatic structure in Fleet Street he had just humanized with appropriately theatrical decoration.)

Atkinson was essentially a product of the Edwardian period and its highly sophisticated, highly intelligent attitude to style and to history. He also had a particular talent for ornament and detailing. He was widely travelled and open to foreign influences. Atkinson was, therefore, typical of his generation in his equivocal attitude to modern architectural development, welcoming the achievements of engineers and technical advances while staying determined to maintain the valuable qualities represented by style, tradition and decoration. For him, the architect had to remain an 'artist' – a balance which it was possible to maintain with distinction in the 1930s but which later became more difficult. In the austere post-war years, with economic stringency and the Modern Movement in the ascendant, Atkinson's generation found itself in an unsympathetic climate, obliged, by

3 Atkinson and Bagenal, *op.cit.*, p.1.
4 Interview with Atkinson, 'Local Artists no.6' in *Richmond & Twickenham Times*, 1 October 1932.

necessity, to produce less interesting and convincing work. Although Atkinson's own peculiar sympathy for the Georgian period found useful expression in the restoration of bomb-damaged buildings, he did not have the scope really to flourish again as an architect. But if Atkinson was typical of his generation in many respects, what was distinctive about him? One thing was certainly his skill as a teacher and organizer. He was a dynamic figure and a catalyst, bringing out the best in Hope Bagenal and Frank Yerbury and others at the Architectural Association. He was also remarkable as a perspectivist in an era when that particular art form was at its apogee of glamour and sophistication.

Atkinson came to London from Nottingham in 1905 and soon established a reputation as a talented architectural draughtsman, especially after winning the Soane Medallion in 1906 for his paper realization of Bacon's 'ideal palace'. He also worked in some of the best offices: those of John Belcher, then celebrated for the quality of the assistants; C. E. Mallows, the country house architect, who was himself an accomplished perspectivist; and R. Frank Atkinson (no relation). As a result of the connections and friends thus made, Atkinson was able to rely on perspective work after he set up in practice in 1907. Perspectives were then important, both for presentation of a scheme to a client and, above all, for annual exhibition at the Royal Academy. Several accomplished perspectives by Atkinson, both signed and unsigned, graced the walls of the Architecture Room at the Summer Exhibition over the next few years, illustrating designs by, amongst others, Aston Webb, Frank Atkinson, Mallows and Dan Gibson, the architectural partner of the landscape gardener and planner, Thomas Mawson. Mawson also employed Atkinson's skills when he asked him to draw chapter headings and other decorations to ornament his splendid book of 1911, *Civic Art*. These delightful black and white pen drawings were essentially architectural fantasies on classical themes.

Reilly well describes the character of the office at 2 Gray's Inn Square that Atkinson shared with George Nott and two other superb draughtsmen, Charles Gascoyne and Alick Horsnell.

These four made not only a cheery set of companions but, between them, a very powerful team. They lived, like most young men did in those days, 'by taking in washing' – to use the architectural slang then prevalent. This meant they were willing to design anything from a palace to a pigsty for any architect not anxious to, or perhaps not capable of, designing it himself. They would design, and then make drawings of any and every kind, from Royal Academy perspectives to working drawings and full-size details. When some provincial architect knocked at the door and asked for Mr Atkinson, all the others would temporarily be his assistants, or really so if necessary. Sometimes the giver-out of washing could not come to terms, and would then go away and consult his list of recommended ghosts, often turning up again to the same office and this time asking, say, for Mr Gascoigne [sic], when all the others would in turn become his most obsequious assistants. The man who eventually landed the job would charge perhaps five shillings an hour for the work and then sub-let the work, or part of it, at four shillings and sixpence an hour to his friends. A great deal of work was done in this way in this office. It was a merry life, with great rushes of work as the time for sending in for the Academy drew near... [in 1910, incidentally, Atkinson was apparently charging fifteen guineas for a large coloured pespective]. No one, however, even in those days, went on being a ghost forever. Someone got to know the truth and employed the ghost direct. [5]

But before 1912, when Atkinson entered into partnership with George Alexander and his professional career really took off, 'ghosting' was important. He did a certain amount of work for his former employer, R. Frank Atkinson, including producing his design for the County Hall competition and decorative work at the Adelphi Hotel in Liverpool — the latter executed in a smart Louis XVI ocean liner style which he further developed at the Gresham Hotel in Dublin. This was not officially acknowledged, nor was Atkinson's hand in designing the new premises for John Barker & Co. for the firm's in-house architects. Thomas Mawson, however, did acknowledge Atkinson's collaboration in his planned 'Improvement' of the town of Bolton in 1910, for Mawson had neither the skill nor the knowledge to produce the design of the proposed museum overlooking the grand new boulevard in the fashionable American 'Grand Manner'.

This scheme for Bolton was published in *Civic Art*, a supreme British expression of that Edwardian desire to combine monumental classic architecture with the grand Parisian tradition of urban planning. The replanning and rebuilding of cities involving the erection of new public buildings in the Grand Manner were the obsessions of Atkinson's generation both before and after the First World War. Atkinson himself never had the opportunity to realize such ideals. His own essay in civic art was unfortunately timed and never built. This was the Bath Improvement Scheme of 1916, an attempt to enhance the centre of the city with new axial open spaces and public monuments in sympathy with its Georgian traditions. The presentation drawings — both plans and perspectives — were a *tour de force* of architectural draughtsmanship.

Atkinson was unusual in being a sensitive colourist as well as a fine draughtsman. So important did he consider the subject of colour in architecture that he put it on the curriculum at the AA. Indeed, Atkinson was that rare phenomemon: a good architect who was also a successful interior designer. Furthermore, he was an interior designer with a particular feeling for public places, especially the theatre. This talent was developed in the provincial cinemas he designed over a period starting before the First World War and culminating in 1921 with the Regent Cinema in Brighton.

The Regent, the first of the 'super-cinemas' embodying experience of American designs, was one of the most remarkable British buildings of the 1920s.[6] Cleverly planned on an awkward site, it ingeniously combined auditoriums with restaurants, bars and other public spaces, all sumptuously and vigorously decorated in a florid Roman style or on particular themes. Atkinson solved a number of problems here for the first time, notably by designing appropriate facades with a very large

5 Reilly, op.cit., p.30.
6 Reilly, op.cit., p.36.

proscenium arch capable of incorporating giant lettering and posters. As Atkinson himself later observed, 'is it not rather stupid to design the front of a theatre to look like a Roman temple and then carve it up with posters and moving electric signs, so that the Roman temple disappears behind paper and lamps?'[7] One critic noted that the Regent was 'recognized as showing that a type of design usually marked by tawdriness and bad taste can be rendered as architecturally excellent as any other, and that without the sacrifice of any practical requirements'.[8] Sadly, the tantalizing interiors of the Regent, richly coloured with murals and decorations by Walter Bayes, Walpole Champneys and Laurence Preston, can now only be appreciated from black and white photographs, but something of their character is conveyed by Atkinson's own vibrantly coloured gouache sketches, which provide yet another example of the all-pervasive influence in Europe of the stage-sets and costumes of Diaghilev's *ballets russes*.

Atkinson's feeling for the theatrical found suitable expression in other projects, notably in 'Fun City' in Salford and in the entrance hall of the Daily Express Building in Fleet Street. In both of these designs, the influence of contemporary America is evident. In Fleet Street, Atkinson was brought in by Lord Beaverbrook to work within the glass- and vitrolite-sheathed concrete frame by Owen Williams. The task was to design a distinctive modern interior that would attract the attention of the passer-by and emphasize that the black building was not just a printing works but also the seat of a powerful press baron. In this, Atkinson was triumphantly successful. He used both reflecting materials and electric light to create a glittering, luminous and sensational effect in a style more usually associated with the cinema. Decorated in gold and silver, with large relief panels by Eric Aumonier and furniture by Betty Joel, this is the only commercial interior in London to compete with the Art Deco skyscraper lobbies of New York.

Atkinson's rare talent in this sphere – his controlled ebullience achieved, often, in new materials – also found an outlet in shop design in the 1930s, notably for the Gas Light & Coke Co., and for Lunn's, the travel agents. His theatrical sense also found happy purpose in his conversion of William Porden's Riding School in Brighton – previously known as the Dome – into a dance and concert hall and banqueting suite. Here, Atkinson's transformed interiors were contemporary in feeling and yet in the spirit of the Oriental-style original buildings and Royal Pavilion opposite. One commentator in 1935 praised this 'magnificent display of fantasy' and noted how 'Mr Atkinson's arsenal of surprise is richer than that of Mr Porden, who was unacquainted with chromium-plating, glazed faience, coloured rubber flooring, neon tubes, and concealed lighting. It is with these that Mr Atkinson has set the latest scene in Brighton's Oriental masquerade'.[9] Indeed, so successful was he in capturing the exotic spirit of Brighton that few realize that some of the Indian-style additions along Church Street and New Road are not early nineteenth century but date from the 1930s.

The work at Brighton exemplifies another remarkable aspect of Atkinson's talent – his ability to design in harmony with work of the past but without slavishly copying past styles. This was also evident in his two executed church designs, each built in

7 R. Atkinson, 'Design in Public Buildings' in John Gloag, ed., *Design in Modern Life*, 1934, p.86.

8 *Architect*, 12 January 1923, p.19.

9 *The Architect & Building News*, 11 January 1935, p.66.

suburban areas with the proceeds of the sale of a church site in the City of London and each incorporating fittings and other elements from the demolished buildings. St Catherine's, Hammersmith, in the middle of the LCC's Old Oak Common Estate, contained the pulpit and organ from the Early Georgian church of St Katherine Coleman, demolished in 1926, in an austere barrel-vaulted classical interior. All Hallows', Twickenham, incorporated not only the fine furnishings, doorcases and other woodwork from Wren's All Hallows', Lombard Street, taken down in 1938, but also used its tall stone tower, joining it to the body of the new church by a cloister which cleverly provided space for the monuments from the old church. Yet nowhere does Atkinson's new building attempt to imitate the style of Wren. The old wood-work sits harmoniously in a spacious round-arched interior with an angular coffered ceiling which deserves comparison with the best church design of the 1930s.

The Twickenham church, in particular, provides the only positive aspect of the scandalous policy of the Diocese of London towards the City churches right through the 1920s and 30s, a period conspicuous for the ruthless demolition of some of the finest Georgian buildings in London. Another, lesser, scandal which concerned the Georgian Group was the destruction of Portland Town, a Late Georgian suburb just north-west of Regent's Park. Here, ironically, several of the new blocks of flats that replaced the stuccoed terraces were designed by Atkinson & Anderson.[10] Between the wars a process of Manhattanizing parts of West London for the wealthy began, encouraged by the belief, shared by both architects and planners, that flats, and not houses, were the answer to the housing problem. (A Dane – Steen Eiler Rasmussen – rather than an Englishman was the principal contemporary dissenter.) Atkinson's entry into this burgeoning sphere of flat-building began in 1935 with the White House off the Marylebone Road, but his principal essays in this building type – Stockleigh Hall and Oslo Court – are to be found overlooking Regent's Park.

None of these blocks can be said to be in sympathy with the former scale and style of this part of London. Most are accomplished essays in that Modernistic, rather American style, with rounded corners and banks of balconies, which became conventional for luxury flats in the 1930s. It is significant – and typical – that in 1937 the RIBA gave its Bronze Medal to Stockleigh Court, a smooth, bland composition with Georgian proportions overwhelmed by *moderne* styling, when nearby Oslo Court is much more interesting and inventive, being close in spirit to the European Modern Movement. This has a brilliant sawtooth plan, with asymmetrical corner windows and balconies skewed from the long side elevations of the long, narrow block, so that each flat has a view of the park. The resulting elevations are busier and more complex than the usual rectilinear expression of contemporary Modern Movement blocks of flats, although there are echoes of Wells Coates, even of Aalto, in the design, Atkinson, however, tempered the angular geometry by using brick, relieved – on the side facing the Park – by little blocks of carved stone ornament, while the whole building was given a fashionable 'nautical' look by banks of round porthole windows.

Oslo Court is certainly one of Atkinson's best buildings and his other blocks of flats are better than the opulent average. Even so, such jobs are not really

10 The June 1938 issue of the *Architectural Review* which illustrated Oslo Court and Stockleigh Hall also carried an article, 'Shutters up in Portland Town' by Ralph Parker, describing the destruction of the area.

representative. Atkinson's origins lay in the classical revival of the Edwardian years and he was happiest designing in a classical manner. His early executed work reflects the preference for English Late Georgian and for neo-Classicism – the 'neo-Grec' – that characterized advanced taste just before the the the First World War, as in the work of Adshead & Ramsay and A. E. Richardson. Atkinson's own great sympathy for the Georgian and his sensitive handling of 'neo-Grec' can be seen in his admirably harmonious conversions and additions to the houses in Bedford Square for the Architectural Association. A similar taste can be seen in his treatment of Percy Lodge, the Georgian house in East Sheen which he filled with his own good collection of antique furniture and paintings. As Reilly noted with approval, 'he lives and works in finely shaped apartments surrounded by fine things. An architect who feels, as he obviously does, that that is the only way to live, is a man whose own work is not likely to fall behind such a standard.'[11]

Atkinson's knowledge of Georgian architecture and, in particular, of the Adam style, can also be seen in the Vaudeville Theatre. His neo-Georgian was not pedantic; rather, it had a crisp, contemporary flavour. Atkinson's new block at the back of the AA in Morwell Street is a solid, sensible essay in the Georgian rational manner, while his Town Hall and Library for Wallington is built not in the stripped classical style in stone so often favoured for municipal buildings between the wars, but has a more humble classical treatment in brick and stone better suited to a suburban Surrey village. That he could also handle the conventional stripped classical treatment with conviction is shown by his post-1945 work at the Croydon Polytechnic.

Atkinson would always choose a style suitable for the job, so it is a mistake to seek consistency in his work. For houses, several treatments were available. His earliest domestic jobs used a conventional free vernacular style. Some later houses employed the urbane Georgian tradition as interpreted by Lutyens, but for the rugged cottages in Cornwall designed for John Betjeman's father, Atkinson showed a clear debt to Voysey. In such buildings, as in his employment of several artists in his more theatrical interiors, he showed the continuing potency of the influence of the Arts and Crafts movement. As with the most intelligent Arts and Crafts architects, style as such did not matter. What interested Atkinson was the sensible use of materials and what he called 'Logic' – the blending of knowledge of the history of architecture, of knowledge of historical ornament and of draughtmanship with the requirements of buildings, *the needs of the people who will inhabit it*'.[12]

As already mentioned, the style of Atkinson's churches was classical rather than Gothic, a choice suggested by the need to incorporate classical church furniture. The steel-framed church in Hammersmith, however, was externally faced in brick in a straightforward Romanesque or Early Christian style fashionable for churches in the 1920s. This church was much admired when new for its simple interior; unfortunately, it was the unhappy victim of a stray German bomb and the austerity of its interior as now conveyed by black and white photographs may be misleading for, as was typical of Atkinson, the white of the plasterwork and the black of the dado were relieved by blue-painted pews and an orange and blue-green baldachino.

11 Reilly, op.cit., p.39.
12 Atkinson's lecture on 'Logic in Architecture', quoted in Lawrence Weaver, *Small Country Houses of Today*, vol.2, 1922, p.196.

Atkinson much admired the work of Sir Giles Gilbert Scott, but if this is not obvious in his churches it is very evident in the two power stations on which he acted as consultant architect. In these post-1945 jobs, the ideal is that of the 'cathedral of power' first realized by Scott at Battersea. The sublime mass of the power stations is not denied but humanized by a careful treatment of the brickwork in a 'jazz modern' manner. The influence of Scott is particularly conspicuous in the Croydon 'B' station at Waddon Marsh, with its vast monumental planes of beautiful brickwork.

Good decorative brickwork is also evident in the Barber Institute in Birmingham. This is a building which again shows the influence of Scott – for its digested traditionalism, horizontality, rounded corners and lack of central emphasis all echo Scott's New Bodleian Library in Oxford, designed shortly before. The Barber at first seems a curious building, impossible to categorize in terms of style, and strangely reticent and understated for a public building. Yet every element shows careful thought and is justified by logic. Everything follows from the practical plan: the brick facing of the first floor is a suitable treatment of the windowless gallery spaces and is clearly distinct from the fenestrated, stone ground floor which contains offices and teaching rooms. The only grand gesture is the giant rectilinear arch enclosing the entrance, a form which is reminiscent of the headquarters of the RIBA and is thus Swedish in origin, although its character in Birmingham seems almost Oriental, even Persian. Such is the effect of sophisticated eclecticism when informed by wide knowledge and governed by logic.

Atkinson was certainly familiar with modern Swedish architecture, which had widespread influence in the 1920s, especially at the Architectural Association, where it was encouraged by Howard Robertson and Frank Yerbury through tours and articles. It is therefore interesting to find that Walter Ison, in writing an obituary for the Regent Cinema in Brighton, recalled that it was 'a building which, apart from Easton and Robertson's Royal Horticultural Hall, was the only British building of its time to receive the unstinted admiration of a visiting party of Swedish architects whose standards were the works of Östberg, Tengbom and Asplund.'[13]

The Regent Cinema was clearly Atkinson's masterpiece and it is a tragedy that it has been destroyed. His talent for dramatic and exuberant interior decoration – rare in the respectable end of the architectural profession between the wars – can still be enjoyed at the Daily Express, but even here his name tends to be overshadowed by that of Owen Williams. Because Atkinson did not design any conspicuous or well-known building, and because his architecture was often understated in character as well as subtly eclectic, his work is still not taken sufficiently seriously. This is a pity. Nevertheless, Sir John Summerson considers that 'the Barber Institute represents better than any other building (except, perhaps, the RIBA in Portland Place) the spirit of English architecture in the 1930s'.[14] A survey of the rest of its designer's output might suggest that Robert Atkinson was one of the most representative as well as one of the most interesting British architects of the whole confused and much misunderstood inter-war period.

13 Walter Ison, article in the Journal of the Decorative Art Society, no.6, 1981, pp.31-6.
14 John Summerson, 'The Architecture of British Museums and Art Galleries' in J. Chapel and C. Gere, eds., The Fine and Decorative Art Collections of Britain and Ireland, 1985, p.18.

ROBERT ATKINSON AND THE ARCHITECTURAL ASSOCIATION   *Alan Powers*

Robert Atkinson's appointment in January 1913 as the Head of the Architectural
Association School came at a moment when architectural education was an issue of
passionate interest in the profession. Since 1901, when the AA Day School had
opened under A. T. Bolton, new schools had been founded throughout the country,
while existing schools had expanded their range, offering two-year full-time
courses and additional evening classes on a scale not previously known. Student
drawings were published in the architectural papers, and methods of training were
hotly debated.

Atkinson's predecessor, H. P. G. Maule, had resisted the tendency, led from
Liverpool by Professor C. H. Reilly, to emulate the American version of Beaux-Arts

entrance hall

with its ideal of monumental neo-Grec. Reilly in turn made no secret of his contempt for Maule's Arts and Crafts approach. His criticisms were unjust, but in February 1912 they led the Council of the AA to commission a report which called for 'a man who is known for his powers of design'. Maule resigned towards the end of 1912 and Atkinson, who had taught the newly established Third Year in Architectural Design since 1911, succeeded him. His experience in a number of Paris ateliers and his draughting ability (then a much sought-after quality in schools) would have recommended him for the post.

As Atkinson recalled, 'When I began at the AA... we were really enthusiastic about things. It was neo-Grec, neo-Roman, neo-Beaux-Arts, neo-American, neo-

dining room (now the main lecture hall on the ground floor)

anything.'[1] R. A. Duncan, a student of the time who joined the staff in the 1920s, remembered that: 'Teachers were drawn from Paris or the 1st Atelier in Wells Mews. The Library was filled with illustrations of the Beaux-Arts Prize Drawings. Many French ideas on monumental planning and also presentation were grafted onto the previous, somewhat restricted, outlook of the English Domestic Tradition. The School became rather exuberantly French in patches.'[2] Many of the young teachers, such as Robert Cable, Alan Potter and Walter Keesey, are now forgotten figures, but L. H. Bucknell, one of those drawn in fresh from the 1st Atelier, remained at the AA in the 1920s and designed classical and Modernist buildings of distinction.

In the summer of 1914, Howard Robertson, a former pupil from the Maule era,

1 Robert Atkinson's speech at his retirement dinner, *Architectural Association Journal*, XLV, 1929, p.396.

2 R. A. Duncan, 'Review of Exhibition of Student Drawings', 1929, *ibid.*, p.67.

returned from Paris to transform the Evening School into a fashionable 'atelier' which, with others like it, was intended to be the basis of an English Beaux-Arts system. The rapid and rather superficial assimilation of Beaux-Arts ideas was encouraged by Atkinson, and indeed reflected in his own architecture. Student designs published in 1913 and 1914 are in line with the norm imposed by Reilly through the Board of Architectural Education and the newly created Rome Scholarship in Architecture, but they show a sad falling off in domestic design, while a scheme for a 'Design for a Church Tower in the Manner of Wren' reveals the severance of long-standing links with the English classical tradition. A telling item from the records of the time is the making of films to show building construction – a far cry from the building trade classes and handling of materials which had been the rage in the 1890s.

The Architectural Association furthered links with France with an exhibition of designs from the Ecole des Beaux-Arts and a visit of French architectural students in 1913, followed by a return visit of AA students and an exhibition of contemporary British architecture in Paris in 1914. Atkinson felt that the War came too soon for his new regime to be properly assessed, and in 1914 he admitted that the imitation of Beaux-Arts work tended to perpetuate the worst features of the original, although he felt, as did Reilly, that as a system it gave a discipline previously lacking in England.

Atkinson was exempted from war service and remained in his post at the AA,[3] assisting in the move in 1917 from Tufton Street to Bedford Square, where he made a number of alterations. In the Library, he designed Adamesque bookcases and an overmantel with a scrolled pediment which shows a freedom in the mixing of a contemporary style with that of the original 1776 building. His studio block in Morwell Street, on the other hand, displays a utilitarianism appropriate to its function and position.

In October 1919, Atkinson became Director of Education, with Howard Robertson as Principal. This gave him overall control of the curriculum and appointments without taking all his time from practice. It is hard to separate Atkinson's contribution to the AA from Robertson's; they seem to have thought along very similar lines. The other key figure remaining from the Tufton Street era was the Secretary, Frank Yerbury. He had gone, dressed in top hat, to invite Atkinson to join the AA staff, only to be asked 'Why are you wearing that damn thing?'[4] Atkinson, Robertson and Yerbury set the debonair style for the school, and the admission of female students in 1920 added considerably to the social life.

In the 1920s, the position of the Beaux-Arts in schools was consolidated. At Liverpool, Reilly continued to admire American Classicism uncritically, while in 1919, Atkinson inspected the major American schools of architecture for the RIBA. Comparing their facilities and standards of achievement with those in England, he conceded their superiority, but in his report, published in 1922, he sounded a number of warning notes about the selectivity of the training and its failure to integrate technical and aesthetic considerations. He added, however, that he felt American architecture was about to embark on a new and less academic phase,

3 After a hearing on 23 August 1916, Atkinson was exempted from military service on the grounds that 'serious hardship would ensue if the man were called up for Army service, owing to his exceptional financial business obligations and domestic position'. He was then the sole remaining member of the partnership based at 199 Piccadilly, as the Junior Partner (Alexander) and the rest of the staff were all serving. He was also married with one child (John). Atkinson was passed fit for garrison duty at home only.

4 F. R. Yerbury, 'Robert Atkinson', *Architectural Association Journal*, LXVIII, 1953, p.120.

members' room

and revealed a concern with architecture as part of general culture. 'Everywhere in America one is struck by the interest taken by the public in architecture, and more important still, in good architecture... They have connected architecture soundly with the cultural development of their nation. (Can we say as much for the English schools?)'[5] Under Atkinson, the Architectural Association in fact provided an education in architecture and design which formed the basis for a number of distinguished non-architectural careers. It also participated in a successful movement to make architecture a matter of greater public awareness and concern. It held notable exhibitions, among them a 1924 show of Swedish architecture with a specially made model of Stockholm Town Hall, and a 1921 display of Claud Lovat

5 Robert Atkinson, *Report on the Education of the Architect in the United States of America*, 1922, p.4.

19

Fraser's sets for the *Beggar's Opera*, which clearly influenced Atkinson's colour schemes for the Regent Cinema.

Students of the time who later gave their allegiance to the Modern Movement, like J. M. Richards and Geoffrey Jellicoe, have described the curriculum as uninspiring and full of unrealistic problems, and even a traditionalist contemporary, Stephen Dykes Bower, has no better memories of it. Howard Robertson, introducing the AA students' *Book of Design* of 1924, described the foreign influences then sweeping the School and the profession as an unavoidable condition of the time, to be countered with principles of abstract design, the logic of planning and a deeper knowledge of styles.

Atkinson was from a generation for whom eclecticism was perfectly natural: his task as a pedagogue, therefore, was to clarify principles. *Theory and Elements of Architecture* of 1926 was the first part of a projected treatise by Atkinson and the Librarian, Hope Bagenal. It is based on Atkinson's lectures, but also reflects Hope Bagenal's subtle and thoughtful amassing of architectural knowledge (for Raymond Erith, Hope Bagenal was the most inspiring member of staff). In the opinion of John Brandon-Jones, it is 'the best book on the subject ever written in English'.[6] It is certainly a deeper study than the other works of theory by Howard Robertson, Trystan Edwards and Arthur Stratton which were published in the 1920s to supply the burgeoning architectural schools. The book marks the last period in which a continuous theory of architecture could be derived from buildings of all previous cultures, without the sense of *tabula rasa* insisted on by the Modern Movement. It is notable for the interaction of anthropology and exact observation which informs the division of architecture into a series of 'elements' such as walls, windows and roofs – the combination of which was to have been explored in subsequent, unpublished, volumes. The work as it stands, however, provides a fine basis for understanding traditional English architecture in the twentieth century, with its strong emphasis on common sense and its joint allegiance to the vernacular, the Arts and Crafts movement and Classicism. Reading it, one can see why the Architectural Association was the starting-place of the Building Centre, which bridged the transition to Modernism. The most advanced designs in the book are sketches by Mendelsohn, illustrated with the caveat 'A small mind will not become great by changing its mode from "Classic" to "Modern" or by using cantilevers instead of beams… Architecture advances, as we have said, by very slowly making use of the best and most universal experiments.'[7]

Although Atkinson and Hope Bagenal stressed the particular qualities developed over time for building in the English climate, the most notable feature of the Architectural Association in the 1920s was the continuing waves of foreign influences, chiefly from Scandinavia and Holland, which were nourished by Yerbury's tours and photographs. These influences show clearly in the designs (all by former AA students or staff) which were chosen by Atkinson as an assessor in the competitions for the Shakespeare Memorial Theatre, the RIBA Building and Norwich City Hall. Yet all these buildings also display the rigorous and imaginative planning which, more than any particular stylistic exclusions or selections, was the basis of the School's teaching.

Atkinson retired from his post as Director of Education in 1929 as part of a restructuring

Morwell Street entrance

6 'Bliss was it in that dawn to be alive', an interview with John Brandon-Jones, in *Architectural Design*, Profile 24, 'Britain in the Thirties', Gavin Stamp, ed., p.97.

7 Robert Atkinson and Hope Bagenal, *Theory and Elements of Architecture*, 1926, p.361.

Morwell Street studios

of the School, leaving Robertson in charge of the initially painless transition to a more radical Modernism. It is interesting to speculate how he might have coped with the crisis in the School in 1938 when the Council tried to reverse the trend towards sociological and collaborative architecture: then, Atkinson's friend H. S. Goodhart-Rendel went down fighting for individual design skills, a cause to which Atkinson was equally committed.

Atkinson's time at the Architectural Association was a complicated, transitional period, when schools were divided over the issues of Modernism. As an educationist, he gave shape and form to this period, which is still very little admired and even less understood.

Bath improvement scheme, 1915

Bath Improvement Scheme (1915–16; unexecuted)

For Bath City Council.

Atkinson was appointed to report on how the bathing and entertainment facilities in Bath might be extended, to advise on the provision of a civic centre in keeping with the city's reputation as Britain's foremost watering place, and to prepare a plan showing the general street improvements necessary. The main proposal of his report, presented in January 1916, was the provision of a new focal point for the city in the shape of a Forum opening through colonnades onto new baths, a concert hall and a large hotel. At the northern end the Forum was to be closed by the Abbey Church, and at the southern end by the concert hall. The report shows his great sensitivity as an architectural historian and town planner and his concern for well-informed and sympathetic building in a historic environment. After the First World War, in 1919, a sub-committee was set up by the Council to consider the report, but no action was taken on it. Nevertheless, the project secured Atkinson a reputation as a town planner since some of the designs were exhibited in 1916 and 1917 at the Royal Academy and in 1922 in Dublin, prompting the *Irish Builder and Engineer* to remark that: 'with a few others, like Professor Richardson, Professor Reilly, etc., [Atkinson]... has been largely responsible for the revival of the academic architecture of recent years.' The designs were also shown at the RIBA and provincial centres as part of a 1936 exhibition on the theme of civic centres.

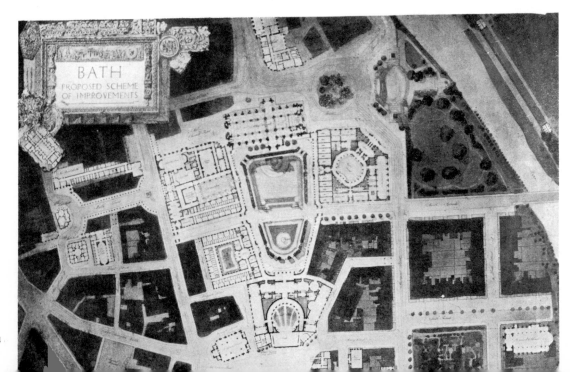

DECORATIVE PAINTING

PAINTED BAND

PLASTER GRILL

DEVELOPED

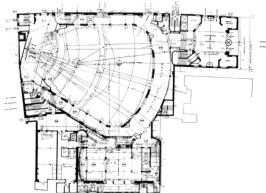

NORTH STREET

The Regent, Queen's Road, Brighton
(1919–21; 1923; demolished 1974)

For Provincial Cinematograph Theatres Ltd.

One of the first super-cinemas after the American model: Atkinson spent eleven weeks in the United States before embarking on the project, which contained – in addition to a fan-shaped auditorium seating nearly 3,000 people in stalls and balcony – spacious foyers and promenades, a restaurant, cafés and a large, rooftop winter garden (finally opened as a ballroom in 1923). Its exterior frontage onto Queen's Road consisted of a great glazed proscenium which ran up through three storeys and revealed the Italian restaurant on the second floor. The

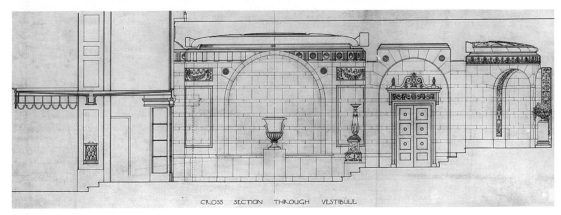

CROSS SECTION THROUGH VESTIBULE

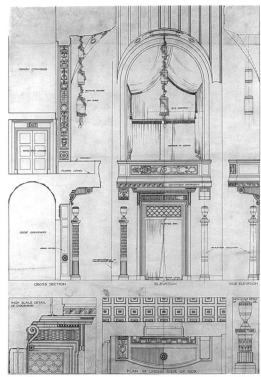

opening was surrounded by stonework of different colours and embellished with classically derived motifs. Within the auditorium, the predominant colour was orange and throughout the building Atkinson could be seen at his most colourful and decorative. His designs included paintings by Walter Bayes, Walpole Champneys and Laurence Preston. Discussing the building in the *Architectural Review* of 1921, Stanley Adshead praised the decoration and colour scheme, adding that Atkinson was recognized as, perhaps, the finest colourist in the profession. The Regent made Atkinson's name — not least on account of his great success in handling the awkwardness of its irregular site. 'It was his No. 1 Symphony, one whose every movement was instinct with vitality', Howard Robertson wrote in the *RIBA Journal* in 1953 (vol.LX, p.117).

27

St Catherine's Church, Hammersmith, London (1922–3; destroyed 1940)

For the Diocese of London.

The church was built from the proceeds of the sale of the site of the eighteenth-century St Katherine (sic) Coleman, Fenchurch Street, which was closed in 1921 and demolished 'on structural grounds' in 1926 to make way for offices. All interior fittings from the church considered worthy of preservation, including the elegant pulpit, were re-erected in the new church. They provided a rich constrast with its otherwise plain interior, consisting of one large barrel-vaulted hall. The exterior, of London stocks, was similarly unadorned, with round-arched windows, minimal detailing and pantiled roof – together giving a hint of the Early Christian style. A steel frame was used – the first instance of this in British church architecture – and as a result costs were greatly reduced, with construction taking only just over six months. The church held about 540 people and was consecrated on 24 February 1923. On 14 September 1940 all but the apse was destroyed by enemy action, and that had to be demolished later on grounds of safety. (A new church was built on the site by the architect's son John Atkinson and consecrated in 1959.)

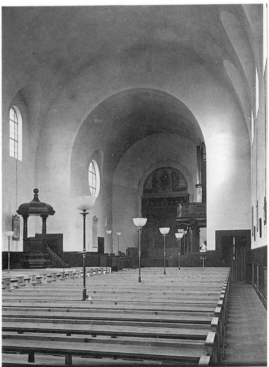

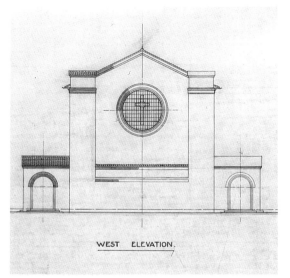

WEST ELEVATION.

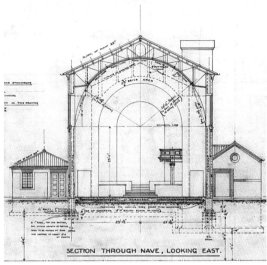

SECTION THROUGH NAVE, LOOKING EAST.

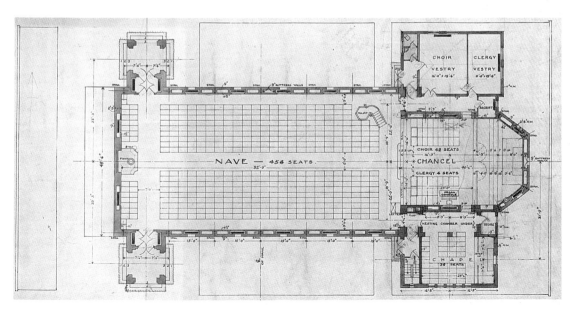

NAVE — 454 SEATS.

CHOIR VESTRY

CLERGY VESTRY

CHOIR 42 SEATS

CHANCEL

CLERGY 4 SEATS

HEATING CHAMBER UNDER

STORE

CHAPEL 39 SEATS

29

Amusement Park and Trades Exhibition Hall, Salford, Greater Manchester (1927; not executed)

The building was to have been on the old Cattle Market site, with its principal elevation to Cross Lane. The land was leased for development to Central Midland Trust Ltd., but the project was over-ambitious – the Exhibition Hall was to have been 100 feet high and 500 feet long, with a capacity of 52,000 people – and by the mid 1930s it had lapsed. Nevertheless, the design merits praise for its adventurous originality and sheer sense of fun. Its most noteworthy feature was the reinforced-concrete roof of the Exhibition Hall, for which Sir Owen Williams was the consulting engineer. The roofspan was 230 feet, which allowed for a very large floor space unobstructed by columns – Williams' ideas were influenced by airship hangars. As well as the main hall, this part of the building was to have contained a restaurant and a theatre to seat 3,000. The adjacent amusement park would have been a direct forerunner of the modern theme park. It boasted a 'Native Village', a 'Harem' and a water chute and games stalls, which included a 'House of Nonsense' and an 'Einstein House'! The monumental eye-catching entrance was described by the *Architect and Building News* in the following terms when its design was exhibited at the Royal Academy: 'delightful in its freshness and originality. One can scarcely conceive of a portal so expressive of the idea of fun … and … the more praiseworthy inasmuch as Mr Atkinson has disdained to use traditional motifs of ornament, but has drawn on his imagination for the flamboyant shapes which are here so effectively composed.'

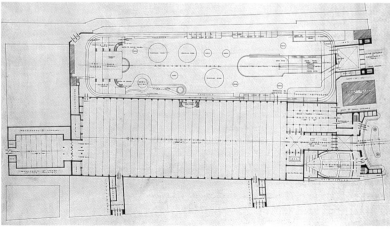

Daily Express Building, Fleet Street, London. Entrance Hall (1931–2)

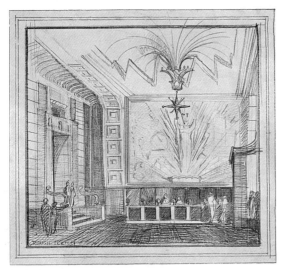

The official architects were Ellis and Clarke but the essential design of the building as a whole must be ascribed to Sir Owen Williams, the consulting engineer. Atkinson's part was limited to the entrance hall which, in contrast to the uncompromising modernity of its housing, is perhaps the best surviving example of Art Deco decoration in Britain. He secured the commission through the newspaper owner Lord Beaverbrook, for whom he had already carried out work at The Vineyard (1919), Cherkley Court (c.1920 and later), Stornoway House (c.1925) and Bedford Lodge (1928). The building as a whole immediately attracted much attention from the protagonists of Modernism, led by Serge Chermayeff who, in an article in the *Architectural Review*, compared

it most favourably to its neighbour, the recently erected stripped classical *Daily Telegraph* Building by Elcock and Sutcliffe. His praise did not, however, extend to Atkinson's contribution, which he described as 'a mass of fibrous plaster, gilded and silvered in the tinsel manner [which] suggests, to me, a provincial "picture palace", an effect which is heightened by two bas-reliefs, left and right, which would make excellent Garbo posters'. The two large plaster panels, intended to represent the British Empire, were carved by Eric Aumonier and are picked out in various shades of gold and silver relieved with touches of colour. The hall's plain wall surfaces and plaster ceilings are in tones of silver and pale green: indirect lighting is concealed along the lower edges of the beams and around the irregular contour of the fluted ceiling. A large beam running across the hall is encased in 'Birmabright' metal with the coffers picked out in gold leaf, and at either end the wall surfaces are faced with polished travertine marble. All this makes a stark contrast indeed with the minimal black vitrolite of the exterior and the functional reinforced concrete of the rest of the building. It shows Atkinson at his most exuberant, luxuriating in the opportunity to develop a side of his creativity expressed at the Regent Cinema, Brighton (1921–2), but stymied by the rejection of his designs for the British Pavilion at the Exposition des Arts Décoratifs, Paris (1925) and the ill-fated Amusement Park and Trades Exhibition Hall in Salford (1927). Despite fulsome praise lavished from other quarters, Chermayeff's criticism of the hall was not unique. Evelyn Waugh was surely caricaturing it in *Scoop* (1933) when he described Lord Copper's Daily Beast Building, Copper House, as having a 'Byzantine vestibule and Sassanian lounge', which caused his protagonist, William Boot, to think 'at first that he must have arrived at some new and less exclusive rival of the RAC'. Forty years later, in *The Buildings of England, London*, I, Pevsner contrasted the hall unfavourably with the rest of the building.

Dome Hall of Music and Corn Exchange, Brighton (1934–5)

Additions and alterations for the County Borough of Brighton.

The Dome was originally the stables of the first house on the site of the Royal Pavilion, and the Corn Exchange was the riding house. Both buildings were by William Porden and date from the first decade of the nineteenth century. In 1850, along with the rest of the Royal Pavilion Estate, they were purchased by the Town Commissioners. The stables were transformed in 1867 into a concert or assembly hall, while the riding house was used as a corn exchange and for other purposes. After the First World War, it was decided to convert them for use as venues for concerts, exhibitions and other events. Perhaps in recognition of his highly acclaimed Regent Cinema (1919–21) in the same town, Atkinson was first nominated in 1932 as technical adviser to the project, and later appointed architect. Early in 1934 a start was made on the Corn Exchange. A new entrance was created in Church Street and partitioning was removed from the interior. Original windows were restored, corresponding mirrors introduced on the opposite wall and the floor relaid in maple for dancing. Kitchens and a supper room, now the Pavilion Theatre, were added, with access from the main banqueting hall by staircases and a gallery, and a separate entrance in New Road. The work was completed by the end of the year. The new entrance continued Porden's frontage and repeated his Saracenic crenellations along the skyline in yellow brick with reconstructed stone details. Above the entrance, in a recessed blue tympanum, are sculpted figures in gold and yellowish brown by James Woodford (1893–1976) and George Jennings Ltd. Over the pavement projected a grey metal canopy (since much altered), supported by black cast-iron standards with red spirals and gold balls; its fascia was decorated with wavy yellow neon tubes. Within, the banqueting hall was also treated in brilliant colours, with blue horizontal fillets covering the joints of the white wood walls and pilasters picked out in red, blue-green and yellow with white and gold capitals. The rafters were green, white and red. These colours were restored in 1983. The designs as a whole are a further demonstration of Atkinson's bent for highly decorative work in appropriate settings. (See catalogue of works, the unexecuted British Pavilion for the Exposition des Arts Décoratifs, Paris (1925); and pp. 32-3, the Daily Express Building (1931–2).) Work began on the Dome, which immediately adjoins the Corn Exchange, on 1 December 1934, and it was formally opened on 14 September 1935. Externally, the original appearance was preserved, indeed enhanced, by the removal of previous alterations. Inside, however, the building was transformed: the cast-iron supports of the domed roof were removed and replaced with iron stanchions – a move which increased its diameter from 80 feet to 125 feet. The seating was almost doubled to 3,000, and a raked floor installed for improved vision at concerts. (When the Dome was used for dancing or exhibitions this could be replaced by a temporary flat floor.) The roof level was lowered by 21 feet and a new cantilevered balcony was built. Walnut panelling covered the walls at the back and in general the colours were kept subdued to harmonize with this since, in Atkinson's words, 'the building is of such a large size that anything of a jazz nature would be probably overwhelming'. Discreet reference was made, however, to the Indian inspiration of Porden's exterior. Atkinson was advised on the acoustics of the hall by Hope Bagenal. It was lit by concealed flood-lighting throughout.

'The White House' (Albany Court), Albany Street, Regent's Park, London (1935–6)

For Sir Lindsay Parkinson & Co. Ltd.

The site is a prominent island bounded by Albany Street, Osnaburgh Terrace, Osnaburgh Street and Longford Street. The building was intended as a response to the new demand for small flats for bachelors and married couples; of the original 758 flats, 626 were one-room. For communal use there were squash courts and a swimming pool in the basement, and a dance floor, restaurant and large public lounges on the ground floor — highly innovatory features for such a building at the time. The floor plan, freely borrowed from Waterhouse's nearby University College Hospital (1897–1906), is star-shaped, or, more precisely, that of an X bisected by an additional wing. This avoided gloomy internal courts and the attendant sense of being overlooked, and gave maximum street frontage. The building was constructed on a reinforced-concrete frame and faced externally in faience slabs — such cladding had already been used by Atkinson at Broadwalk Court (1934) and was typical of contemporary cinema architecture. Perhaps more than any other building, the White House demonstrates Atkinson's success as a commercial architect in the later 1920s and the 1930s. As an early British instance of the 'city within a city', it antedates Gordon Jeeves' Dolphin Square, Pimlico, by one year. It became something of a landmark in the years immediately before the Second World War. In 1976–7, however, it was transformed into a hotel by R. Seifert and Partners, with considerable alterations to its interior, though little structural work.

Oslo Court, Prince Albert Road, Regent's Park, London (1936–7)

A seven-storey block of 125 two-room flats situated on a triangular island site whose acutest corner is opposite the park. By an ingenious system of staggering and grouping each flat around a balcony, Atkinson succeeded in giving almost all of them a park view. (A similar 'democratic' system was used by Lubetkin and Tecton at Highpoint I (1933–5) and later by J. L. Martin and R. Matthew in the arrangement of the boxes at the Royal Festival Hall.) As at Regency Lodge (1935–7) the facing materials are brick, with artificial stone dressings. The steps and surround to the main entrance are in travertine marble. A restaurant for the residents was provided on the ground floor. A six-storey vertical window lights the main staircase and lift halls, while the basement houses an underground garage.

178–180 Edgware Road, London.
Offices and Showrooms for the Gas Light & Coke Company (1936–8; demolished)

The building stood on the east side of the Edgware Road, near the junction with Marylebone Road. Atkinson was consultant architect to the Gas Light & Coke Co. For the exterior he designed a monumental two-storey facade, whose upper section was recessed to contain a fountain and clock. The front was faced with travertine, except for black vitreous around the clock and marble for the door surround. The clock and fountain immediately became local landmarks. The face of the clock was in aluminium with the signs of the zodiac mounted on it in polished brass. At the centre, the dial was pierced, with a loudspeaker behind. The hours and minutes lit up at night. The bowl of the fountain was also in aluminium, with neon tubing as synthetic jets of water. As a piece of exuberant decoration, the exterior is comparable with Atkinson's new entrance to the Corn Exchange, Brighton (1934–5; see pp. 34–5). Inside, the ground floor was given over to the main showroom, while upstairs was a demonstration theatre whose style and layout recalled Atkinson's work as a cinema designer. The Gas Light & Coke Company was incorporated into the North Thames Gas Board in 1948. Renovations carried out by the Board in 1955–7 included the removal of the fountain and clock on the facade and the conversion of the demonstration theatre into a staff canteen.

Sir Henry Lunn's Travel Agency,
56 Haymarket, London (1938; demolished)

Redesign of the interior of an earlier building on the corner of Haymarket and Norris Street. The pivotal feature of Atkinson's layout was a pre-existing pier, whose base he concealed by a circular shelf and table fittings, surmounted by an illuminated glass globe with the signs of the zodiac in bronze. Over this rose an inverted mushroom in fibrous plaster with a design showing the heavens in blue. Lighting was concealed in the top of the mushroom.

Bacon's Ideal Palace, 1906

CATALOGUE OF WORKS

Completion dates are shown in parenthesis at the end of the entry.

Abbreviations are as follows:
AAJ Architectural Association Journal
AI Architecture Illustrated
A&BN Architect & Building News
AJ Architects' Journal
AR Architectural Review
BN Building News
BR Builder
CL Country Life
RIBAJ Royal Institute of British Architects Journal

RA indicates drawings exhibited at the Royal Academy.

1904 Design for a crescent in a large city. Unsuccessful submission for the RIBA Tite Prize, but awarded a Bronze Medal in the National Competition of the Board of Education, South Kensington. A neo-Baroque range of buildings set against a swirling, Art Nouveau cloudscape. See *BR*, LXXXVI, 27 February 1904, pp. 226ff.

Design for a covered bridge, modelled on Henry Hutchinson's 'Bridge of Sighs' (1831) at St John's College, Cambridge. Awarded a Silver Medal in the National Competition of the Board of Education. See *BR*, LXXXIX, 14 October 1905, p. 395. RA 1905 (1469).

1905 Designs for a lounge and staircase in a large hotel. Successful submission for the RIBA Tite Prize and Silver Medal winner in the National Competition of the Board of Education. See *BR*, LXXXVIII, 18 February 1905, pp. 180ff.

1906 Designs for Bacon's Ideal Palace. Awarded the Honourable Mention (i.e. placed second) in the RIBA Soane Medallion Competition. See *BR*, XC, 24 February 1906, pp. 200ff. RA 1908 (1690).

1908 Adelphi Hotel, Lime Street, Liverpool (–1914). Atkinson worked intermittently as assistant to the architect, an unrelated namesake, R. Frank Atkinson.

LCC County Hall. Competition design for R. Frank Atkinson.

Glamorgan County Offices, Cardiff. Unsuccessful competition entry (the commission went to E. Vincent Harris and Thomas A. Moodie). RA 1909 (1493).

Cornwall County Offices, Truro. Unsuccessful competition entry (commission won by Silcox and Reay). See *Academy Architecture*, XLVII, 1915, p.48. RA 1909 (1526).

1909 Rivington House ('Roynton Cottage'), near Bolton, Lancashire. Look-out tower in the grounds for W. H. Lever (1st Viscount Leverhulme). An Arts and Crafts design executed in association with T. H. Mawson. See *CL*, CLXXVI, 13 September 1984, p.679; exhibition catalogue, *Lord Leverhulme* , Royal Academy, 1980, no.438. RA 1910 (1628 – as by Mawson).

Berkshire County Council Offices, Reading. Unsuccessful competition entry (commission went to Warwick and Hall). RA 1911 (1695).

c.1909 Lees Court, Faversham, Kent. Alterations, possibly executed in association with T. H. Mawson, who worked on the gardens at this time. See *Academy Architecture*, XLVII, 1915, p.86.

1910 Usher Hall, Edinburgh. Unsuccessful competition entry (the commission went to J. Stockdale Harrison). See *Academy Architecture*, XLVII, 1915, pp.36-7. RA 1911 (1666).

c.1910 Thornton Manor, Cheshire. Garden house for W. H. Lever (1st Viscount Leverhulme) in association with T. H. Mawson. See T. H. Mawson, *Art and Craft of Garden-Making*, 4th edition, 1912, fig.179; *BR*, CVIII, 7 May 1915, p.437 (as by Mawson).

1911 Totteridge Park, Hertfordshire. Alterations and additions for Albert Barratt. See *Academy Architecture*, XLVII, 1915, p.76.

Proposed house, Totteridge. A design showing plans and a perspective for a house in a style reminiscent of Voysey is at the RIBA. See *Academy Architecture*, XLVII, 1915, p.80.

Bolton: A Study in Town Planning and Civic Art. Title-page, frontispiece and five other perspectives, sections and general plan for T. H. Mawson's book, published in 1911. The book set out ambitious planning proposals, known as the 'Bolton Beautiful' scheme, commissioned

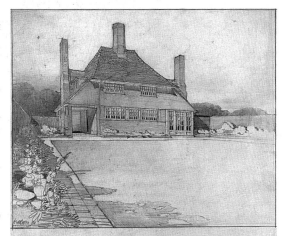

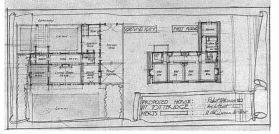

House at Totteridge, 1911

by the 1st Viscount Leverhulme but not adopted by the municipal authorities. The scheme provided Atkinson with an early opportunity to design in the Grand Manner and to work on plans for a new museum and art gallery. See T. H. Mawson, *op.cit.*, title-page, frontispiece and pp.6, 11, 18, 22, 26, 30 and 32; exhibition catalogue, *Lord Leverhulme*, Royal Academy, 1980, p.197, nos.483 and 484.

Civic Art. Illustrations to T. H. Mawson's book, published in 1911 (not to be confused with the preceding entry). Atkinson's frontispiece – the drawing of the proposed museum and art gallery at Bolton – was exhibited at the Royal Academy. The chapter headings he designed have the character of ideal buildings. Atkinson worked intermittently for several years with Mawson, whom he had probably met through C. E. Mallows. See T. H. Mawson,

Central Heating
Pavilion, 1912

op.cit., frontispiece, chapter headings and other illustrations; *Academy Architecture*, XLVII, 1915, pp.46-7; exhibition catalogue, *Lord Leverhulme*, Royal Academy, 1980, p.197, no.483; RA 1911 (1514).

St Marylebone Town Hall. Unsuccessful competition entry (the commission was won by Edwin Cooper). See *Academy Architecture*, XLVII, 1915, p.38. RA 1912 (1759).

New Library and Art Gallery, Piccadilly, Manchester. Unsuccessful competition entry (the commission went to Butler, Crouch and Savage but the project was later cancelled). Atkinson was chosen to go on to the second stage of this competition, which was one of the most important of the period. His design was in a Beaux-Arts style and included a colossal double colonnade on the main front. See *Manchester Guardian*, 15 December 1911. RA 1912 (1724).

1912 Central heating pavilion, Ideal Home Exhibition, Olympia, London. For Phillips and Son Ltd. A garden pavilion in the manner of Lutyens. Atkinson commented in the promotional booklet (*Achievements in Modern Heating and Ventilation*, J. F. Phillips & Son Ltd.): 'It is based on severe classical ideals, though without losing modern feeling and individuality... The main doors themselves are worth passing mention, based as they are upon the Late Georgian townhouse doorway of London, before the advent of rigid neo-Grec and the Gothic Revival extinguished any flickering life which remained in our National Architecture.' See *BR*, CIV, 1913, 4 April, p.404 and 20 June, pp.708ff; *Academy Architecture*, XLVII, 1915, colour plate and p.33. RA 1912 (1734).

Port of London Authority Head Offices, Trinity Square, Tower Hill. Short-listed but ultimately unsuccessful entry in a major competition which had begun the preceding year. The commission went to Edwin Cooper. See *BR*, CIII, 19 July 1912, p.67; *Academy Architecture*, XLVII, 1915, pp.49-52. RA 1913 (1705) and 1914 (1801).

1913 John Barker & Co., Kensington High Street, London (–1914). Rebuilding of department store premises after a fire in 1912. Atkinson was sub-contracted by the in-house architects, Philip Pilditch and H. L. Cabuche. The store was rebuilt once more by Bernard George (1935–9). See *Survey of London*, XLII, 1986, p.88.

Queen's Picture House, Queen's Square, Wolverhampton (–1914; demolished 1980). For Associated Provincial Picture Houses Ltd. Opened on 30 September 1914, the building was in a Beaux-Arts style and contained an 'oak-room café', a lounge and a drawing room-style vestibule

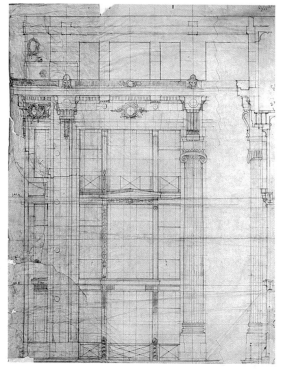

John Barker & Co., London, 1913

with fireplace, in addition to a balconied auditorium seating about 1,000 people. See *BR*, CVI, 26 June 1914, pp.754 and 760; *Academy Architecture*, XLVII, 1915, pp.63-4; N. Williams, *Cinemas of the Black Country*, Wolverhampton, 1982, pp.53-5.

The Picture House, Union Street, Aberdeen (–1914; demolished 1973). For Associated Provincial Picture Houses Ltd. The building opened on 14 December 1914. Its auditorium was similar in design to that at Wolverhampton, though sunk below ground. There was a tapestried tea-room, also at basement level. See *Academy Architecture*, XLVII, 1915, pp.65-8; *BR*, CXIX, 17 September 1920, pp.309-10.

The New Picture House, 56-7 Princes Street, Edinburgh (–1914; demolished c.1954). For Provincial Cinematograph Theatres Ltd. The cinema formed part of the adjoining Royal Hotel, although its monumental superimposed entrance accorded ill with the hotel's Victorian architecture. The auditorium was similar in style to those at Wolverhampton and Aberdeen, though, as befitted its location in the Athens of the North, the interior was more severely classical. See *BR*, CVI, 26 June 1914, pp.754 and 758-60; *Academy Architecture*, XLVII, 1915, pp.53-62 and LII, 1921, 'Theatres and Cinemas', pp.12-13.

The New Picture House, Edinburgh, 1913

'Woodmansterne Corner', Carshalton, Surrey (–1914). The architect's own house, which he described as 'an attempt at American planning on a small scale'. The design has affinities with the domestic work of Voysey and Beresford Pite. See *Academy Architecture*, XLVII, 1915, pp.78-80; *AR*, LI, June 1922, pp.220-2, reprinted in E. and W. G. Newton, eds., *Recent Domestic Architecture*, VI, c.1923, pp.86-8.

1914 'Ridgehanger', Hanger Hill, Ealing (–1915). The house has an L-shaped plan to take advantage of the view over south-west London. It is in a Lutyenesque neo-Georgian style, of grey brick with red dressings and a red, pantiled roof. See *Academy Architecture*, XLVII, 1915, pp.82-4; *AR*, LI, June 1922, pp.216-19; R. Randal Phillips (intro.), *The Modern English House*, Country Life, n.d., p.121; L. Weaver, *Small Country Houses of Today*, II, 1922, pp.194-8. RA 1914 (1857).

Chester House, Belgrave Square, London. Internal refurbishment in Adam style. See *Academy Architecture*, XLVII, 1915, p.87.

18 Bryanston Square, London. Internal and external refurbishment. See *Academy Architecture*, XLVII, 1915, pp.72-5.

The Road Farm, Churt, near Farnham, Surrey. Interior and exterior alterations and layout of the gardens. See *Academy Architecture*, XLVII, 1915, pp.70-1.

Preston Grange, Preston Candover, near Basingstoke, Hampshire (–1918). For General Hope. An Arts and Crafts-style house, originally to have had an adjoining service wing, which remained unbuilt. See *Academy Architecture*, XLVII, 1915, p.77. RA 1914 (1865).

City Picture House, 50 English Street, Carlisle (–1915; demolished 1960). For Associated Provincial Picture Houses Ltd. From a classical frontage of domestic scale in cream faience, a foyer led to a wider, single-storey auditorium in Louis XVI style with seating for 890 people. Above the foyer was a tea-room. This was panelled in oak and hung with tapestry; it sported a fireplace with Dutch tiles and a reproduction Persian carpet. See *Carlisle Journal*, 19 October 1915, p.4 and 5 November 1915, p.7.

The Picture House, Bridge Street, Walsall (work suspended late 1914 and resumed 1918-20; destroyed by fire, 1923). For Associated Provincial Picture Houses Ltd. The front elevation was particularly handsome, faced in cream glazed faience and dominated by marble pillars and columns. Atkinson and Alexander probably acted as consultants; other architects involved were Percy L. Browne and Glover of Newcastle. At the opening of the building (29 July 1920) it was referred to by the Mayor as a 'super-cinema' – no doubt on account of its seating capacity of 1,500 and luxurious interior. This was an early use of the term, which would later be applied to the Regent Cinema, Brighton (1919–21). See N. Williams, *Cinemas of the Black Country*, Wolverhampton, 1982, pp.95-7.

The Picture House, Walsall Street, Wednesbury (–1915; demolished 1938). For Associated Provincial Picture Houses Ltd. The front elevation was in 'Carra ware' and inside, polished wood panelling and tapestries created a luxurious atmosphere. There was seating for 900. See N. Williams, *Cinemas of the Black Country*, Wolverhampton, 1982, p.116.

The Picture House, Stafford Street, Willenhall (–1915;

demolished c.1960). For Associated Provincial Picture Houses Ltd. An unusually modest and functional-looking single-storey building, with seating for 736. See N. Williams, *Cinemas of the Black Country*, Wolverhampton, 1982, p.109.

Board of Trade Offices, Whitehall, London (–1915). Short-listed though ultimately unsuccessful competition entry (the commission went to E. Vincent Harris). See *Academy Architecture*, XLVII, 1915, pp.34-5, 39 and 40-1; *BR*, CVIII, 12 February 1915, pp.147-9f. RA 1915 (1565 and 1605).

Bungalow, Stanley Park Road, Carshalton, Surrey. For Arnold Goldsworthy. See R. Randal Phillips, *The Book of Bungalows*, 1922, p.60.

1915 Bath Improvement Scheme (–1916; unexecuted). For Bath City Council. See p.24 of this publication, as well as *BN*, CX, 8 March 1916, pp.234, 240-1, 247-8; *BR*, CX, 1916, 10 March, pp.199ff and 24 March, pp.234ff; *Architects' & Builders' Journal*, XLIII, 15 March 1916, p.109; *Town Planning Review*, VI, April 1916, pp.272-4; *British Architect*, LXXXVII, May 1916, p.4. RA 1916 (1639, 1641 and 1643); 1917 (1310, 1315 and 1316).

Monument to William J. Plaistowe, Hanwell Cemetery. Executed in Roman marble with ornaments in bronze. See L. Weaver, *Memorials and Monuments*, 1915, pp.444-7.

1917 Architectural Association, 34, 35 and 36 Bedford Square, London (–1919). Alterations to interiors. These were undertaken to provide greater space for the expanding school and included the creation of the Library on the first floor of 34 and 35 Bedford Square, as well as the building of studios in the adjacent mews in Morwell Street. See *BR*, CXXI, 18 November 1921, pp.670-1, also the essay on 'Robert Atkinson and the Architectural Association' on pp.14-21 of this publication.

Proposed open space, London. RA 1918 (1323).

1919 The Regent Cinema, Queen's Road, Brighton (–1921; 1923; demolished 1974). For Provincial Cinematograph Theatres Ltd. See pp.25-7 of this publication; *Academy Architecture*, LIII, 1921, 'The Regent Theatre, Brighton', pp.1-40; *idem*, LIV, 1922, pp.41-56; *AR*, L, November 1921, pp.98-112; *idem*, LIII, April 1923, p.133; *idem*, LXI, April 1927, p.264; *idem*, LXIII, February 1928, p.79; *BR*, CXX, 27 May 1921, p.680; *idem*, CXXI, 1921, 19 August, pp.224-8 and 4 November, pp.599-606; *Graphic*, 14 May 1921, p.587; *British Builder*, XII, April 1925, pp.47-8 and supplement; *Journal of the Decorative Arts Society*

Monument to William J. Plaistowe, Hanwell, 1915

1890-1940, no.6, 1981, pp.31-6; *Picture House*, no.10, Spring 1987, pp.10-14. RA 1920 (1147).

The Vineyard, Hurlingham Road, Fulham, London. Restoration of house and gardens for Lord Beaverbrook. The original house was seventeenth century, with eighteenth-century additions. Atkinson's interior redecoration used bright colours to match modern painted furniture. This was his first commission from Beaverbrook, for whom he worked continually thereafter, at least until 1940. Other works, detailed below, were: Cherkley Court, (c.1920 and later); Stornoway House (c.1925); Bedford Lodge, (1928); Daily Express Building, (1931–2); Mickleham Downs House, (1937); Cricket Court, (undated). See *BR*, CXX, 13 May 1921, p.619; *AR*, LI, June 1922, p.223, reprinted in E. and W. G. Newton, eds., *Recent Domestic Architecture*, VI, c.1923, pp.88-9.

Proposed Theatre and Winter Garden, Clayton Square, Liverpool. See *Academy Architecture*, LII, 1921, p.20. RA 1920 (1179).

c.1920 Cherkley Court, near Leatherhead, Surrey. Alterations and additions for Lord Beaverbrook. Atkinson installed a new indoor swimming pool and renovated the salon as well as executing a new terrace and layout for the gardens. He also undertook other projects – some of them at a later date (see below; 1935). See also *AR*, LVI, November 1924, colour plate following pp.166 and 167. RA 1921 (948, 952 and 956) and 1923 (1198).

'Pound Hill', Balcombe Road, Worth, Crawley, Sussex. For Mrs G. Alexander, wife of Atkinson's former partner. A labour-saving centrally-heated house. See (Anon.), *The Smaller House*, Architectural Press, 1924, pp.150-3.

1922 St Catherine's Church, Hammersmith, London (–1923; destroyed 1940). For the Diocese of London. See pp.28-9 of this publication; *AR*, LIII, June 1923, pp.210-14; *BR*, CXXV, 14 September 1923, p.402f. RA 1923 (1281) and 1924 (1326).

1923 Percy Lodge, Christchurch Road, East Sheen, London. Alterations to house and garden and housing development on the grounds (-1925). Atkinson moved here from Carshalton Beeches in about 1924. The original, small eighteenth-century house had been considerably altered in the nineteenth century, and had fallen into acute disrepair and neglect. In order to rescue it, Atkinson converted the servants' wing into a separate dwelling (lived in briefly by Ralph Knott, the architect of County Hall) and set aside part of the grounds for a colony of houses for artists (John Gloag lived there for the rest of his life). He enclosed his own garden with bricks from Old Devonshire House. Pevsner (see below) noted that the house, which he called the chief survival of pre-Victorian East Sheen, owed a lot to the careful restoration. Atkinson sold the house in 1935. See *CL*, CXXV, 28 May 1959, pp.1210-12; N. Pevsner, *The Buildings of England, Surrey*, 1971, p.206. On the laying-out of the Percy Lodge Estate, see C. H. Reilly, *Representative British Architects*, 1931, p.39; *AR*, LXIV, December 1928, p.281; F. R. Yerbury, *Small Modern English Houses*, 1929, pls.I-XIII; H. de C. Hastings, ed., *Recent English Domestic Architecture*, 1929, p.49; P. Abercrombie, ed., *The Book of the Modern House*, 1939, p.113.

Malone House, near Belfast. Restorations and improvements for Mr W. Barnett, a wealthy grain merchant. The house, originally built in the early nineteenth century, was burnt out by the IRA in 1976.

'Pantiles', 48 Wildwood Road, Hampstead Garden Suburb, London. For Gregory Brown. The house, in neo-Georgian style, has five bays, a central entrance and a hipped roof. This became the accepted style for the wealthier houses in the suburb after the First World War; Pevsner, in *The Buildings of England, Middlesex*, deemed the present house the best example.

127-131 Regent Street, London. Proposed rebuilding (–1927).

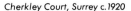
Cherkley Court, Surrey c.1920

In the sketch:
SKETCH FOR THE BRITISH PAVILION AT THE EXHIBITION OF DECORATIVE ARTS PARIS 1925

CANADA
AUSTRALIA
ENGLAND
SCOTLAND

British Pavilion, Paris, 1925

1925 Vaudeville Theatre, Strand, London (–1926). Alterations and redecoration for J. M. and R. Gatti. Atkinson took over as the theatre architect in June. His modifications included gutting the building and reconstructing the auditorium and stage, raising the roof and lowering the basement, and increasing the seating capacity by ninety places. Work began in October 1925 and took only eleven weeks. The front elevation of 1891 was retained on the Strand, but a new one incorporating a Palladian window was built in Maiden Lane at the rear. Further minor work was carried out in 1932 and 1937. See *BR*, CXXX, 19 March 1926, pp.463, 472 and 474-6; *AR*, LIX, April 1926, pp.155-6.

Cameo Cinema ('Cinéma de Paris'), 35-7 Charing Cross Road, London. Reconstruction for Mark Wolfe (–1926). Atkinson's modernization of the building (erected 1909–10) included reconstructing the main entrance on Charing Cross Road and rearranging the seating and staff accommodation.

British Pavilion, Exposition des Arts Décoratifs, Paris. Unexecuted project (commission won by Howard Robertson). The designs which survive from this scheme show Atkinson at his most ebullient and allusive, combining a proscenium entrance with a base of ships' prows, in bright colours and gold.

All Saints' Church, Hindley, Lancashire. Unexecuted design. The present church dates from 1766, but in the 1920s it saw a change of liturgical tradition towards Anglo-Catholicism. Atkinson's lost design may have been connected with alterations then made to the interior. RA 1925 (1140).

23 Sloane Street, Knightsbridge, London. Proposed additions.

47

The Gresham Hotel, Dublin, 1925

The Gresham Hotel, Dublin (–1927). For the Gresham Hotel Company. Rebuilding of a hotel destroyed in fighting between the Government troops of the Free State Army and Anti-Treaty Irregulars in July 1922. Atkinson's elevation, though executed in a different style and on a different scale, has points of contact with the old building, notably in the central attic storey with its urns and volutes. Work began on the new building late in 1925. For the sake of speed, a steel frame was used in its construction. The interiors were in a Louis XVI style, but hardly any of the original decoration now survives. The resident architect was J. V. Downes, who had worked in Atkinson's office in London. See *Irish Builder*, LXVI, 1924, 13 December, p.1037; *idem*, LXVII, 1925, 11 July, p.550, and 21 November, p.230; *idem*, LXVIII, 1926, 20 February, p.113 and 4 September, p.673; *BR*, CXXX, 5 February 1926, pp.229, 232 and 234-5; *idem*, CXXXIII, 16 September

1927, pp.422-5; *AR*, LXI, June 1927, p.216; U. O'Connor, *The Gresham Hotel 1865–1965*, Cork, n.d., *passim*; *AJ*, LXXIV, 25 November 1931, supplement. RA 1926 (1199) and 1927 (1370 and 1377).

c.1925 Stornoway House, Cleveland Row, St James's, London. Interior alterations for Lord Beaverbrook to a house built (1794–6) by Samual Wyatt. Atkinson's work was destroyed when it was bombed in 1940.

1926 'Magna Charta', Wraysbury, Buckinghamshire. Alterations and additions. The original house was built in the early nineteenth century on the supposed site of the signing of the Magna Carta. See *BR*, CXXXII, 14 January 1927, pp.58-9 and 87.

1927 Amusement Park and Trades Exhibition Hall, Salford, Greater Manchester (not executed). See pp.30-1 of this publication; *A&BN*, CXIX, 1928, 27 April, pp.603-5 and

608; *idem*, 11 May, pp.685 and 687; *AR*, LXIII, June 1928, pp.221-2. RA 1928 (1334).

Robindale House, Drax Avenue, Wimbledon. For Mrs Imhof. See *A&BN*, CXXII, 20 September 1929, pp.348-9.

1928 Imhof House, 112-6 New Oxford Street, London (–1929; destroyed). Gramophone shop for Alfred Imhof Ltd. The entire building was occupied by the company but Atkinson was responsible only for the interiors, which included showrooms, a small concert hall and offices. His design for the showrooms, revelling in polychrome metals, pink glass and green, mauve, gold and silver paint, confirmed his position as a leading decorative architect. See *A&BN*, CXXII, 29 November 1929, p.667 and supplement; *AR*, LXVII, May 1930, p.260.

'Grey Ladies' and 'Undertown', Trebetherick, Cornwall. Cottages for E. E. Betjemann (–1929). These were built adjoining a golf course as holiday cottages. The poet John Betjeman, his mother, and his father, Ernest Betjemann, were friends of Atkinson and kept 'Undertown' for their own use. The cottages were built, as far as possible, of local materials – granite and rough-hewn Delabole slates – and traditional detailing was used. For 'Undertown', see *BR*, CXXXVI, 10 May 1929, pp.861 and 877; F. R. Yerbury, *Small Modern English Houses*, 1929, pls.XI-XIII. For 'Grey Ladies', see *RIBAJ*, XLI, 9 December 1933, p.137; E. Carter, ed., *Seaside Houses and Bungalows*, 1937, p.28; R. McGrath, *Twentieth-Century Houses*,

Cottages at Trebetherick, Cornwall, 1928

1934, pp.23 and 90; P. Abercrombie, ed., *The Book of the Modern House*, 1939, pp.54-5.

Bedford Lodge, Newmarket. Alterations and additions for Lord Beaverbrook. The house was bought by Beaverbrook as the base for a brief and unsuccessful venture into racing; he changed its name, no doubt from filial piety, to 'Calvin House'. Atkinson's work included a new loggia and terrace.

39 Newton Road, Westbourne Grove, Bayswater, London. Proposed alterations and additions for E. H. Galsworthy.

Cathanger Manor, Fivehead, Taunton, Somerset. Restorations and additions, including a porch and garage, to buildings dating from the sixteenth and eighteenth centuries. Atkinson rendered the walls with whitewashed Portland cement and retiled the roofs with material found on the site. See *AI*, V, November 1932, pp.150-5.

1929 Memorial chapel and vicarage, Kingsgate, Broadstairs, Kent (unexecuted). The designs seem to have been the pipedream of a wealthy local clergyman. Their style is reminiscent of St Catherine's, Hammersmith (1922–3). See *BR*, CXXXVI, 3 May 1929, pp.808 and 812. RA 1929 (1329).

'Black Firs', Iver Heath, Buckinghamshire. Proposed cottage for Mrs Cronander.

Proposed suburban theatre. RA 1929 (1195).

c.1929 ARP Film Studios, Ealing Green, London (–1931). For Associated Radio Pictures Ltd. Built in response to the introduction of sound films in the late 1920s. Much of the work was by A. F. B. Anderson, Atkinson's partner, who specialized in studio work. Apart from the administration building, the designs were basic and functional, though advanced for their time, notably in sound insulation and air-conditioning. See *AJ*, LXXIV, 16 December 1931, pp.792 and 795-8; *BR*, CXLII, 26 February 1932, pp.392-6.

1930 Store building in London. A competition design (unexecuted). RA 1930 (1380 and 1368).

1931 Demonstration Theatre, 100 Elverton Street, Westminster, London. For Messrs Holophane Ltd. The theatre was built for the sole purpose of demonstrating the clients' colour-lighting system. It was opened by Muriel Angelus, the British film star. See *AJ*, LXXIV, 1 July 1931, pp.28-9.

Daily Express Building, Fleet Street, London. Entrance Hall (–1932). For the Daily Express. See pp.32-3 of this 49 publication; *A&BN*, CXXXI, 1 July 1932, p.14, *AR*, LXXII, July 1932, pp.3-12; *CL*, CLXXXI, 10 September 1987, pp.140 and 142; *Blueprint*, no.41, October 1987, pp.52-4. For the building, see further D. Cottam, *Sir Owen Williams*, Architectural Association, Works III, 1986, pp.61-9.

1932 The Building Centre, 157-8 New Bond Street, London. Exterior and interior alterations (–1933). The Building Centre grew out of the Architectural Association Building Materials Bureau. It opened in September 1932, numbering Atkinson among its original directors. (The others were M. E. Webb (Chairman), F. R. Yerbury (Managing Director), L. H. Bucknell, L. de Soissons, S. Glyn, V. E. Vincent and G. Grey Wornum.) Its purpose, as defined at a meeting of manufacturers and architects held at the RIBA in December 1931, was to provide 'a ready and accessible means whereby the architect and others interested in building may keep themselves abreast of modern developments in building materials and . . . manufacturers may feel certain that their products and their developments are constantly receiving the consideration of the architectural professions, the building industry and the public' (*Forty Years On*, Building Centre Intelligence Report, no.5, 1971, p.3). The conversion of the original premises, the ground, first and second floors of 158 New Bond Street, was confided to Atkinson and H. A. Scott, and after some hesitation Atkinson was also called upon to oversee the modification of the shop front. A few months after the opening, it became clear that the Centre was already too small and a decision was taken, in late 1933, to extend backwards into the Grafton Galleries. These were refitted by Atkinson, who linked them with New Bond Street by a welded-steel bridge. The extension opened in late 1936 and the following year the Centre also took over the lease of a floor next door at 157. Almost all the accommodation was destroyed by bombs in October 1940 and May 1941; shortly afterwards, the Centre moved to temporary quarters provided by the Regent Street Polytechnic.

'Whitebarn', Oxted, Surrey (–1933). For Dr Murray Levick. This was designed as a weekend cottage, adjoining the golf links. Its roof was of pantiles, the gables of whitewashed tilehanging and the lower part of the walls of whitewashed brick. See *RIBAJ*, XLI, 9 December 1933, p.136; R. McGrath, *Twentieth-Century Houses*, 1934, p.90.

Westerham, Kent. Proposed house for Mrs Ethel Watney.

Eros News Reel Cinema, London, 1933

1933 23A and 25 Grove End Road, St John's Wood, London (unexecuted design for houses). For Miss Prentice.

Eros News Reel Cinema, Piccadilly Circus, London (–1934; demolished). For N. J. Hulbert. The building, which stood at the bottom of Shaftesbury Avenue, was converted by Atkinson from the Eros Café for Hulbert's British News Theatres Ltd. The entrance hall was painted brilliant red and black. It had Art Deco figurative friezes at eye-level, picked out in silver and gold. A small, balconied auditorium at basement level, embellished with peach-coloured mirrors and lights, provided seating for just over 200 people. See *A&BN*, CXXXIX, 24 August 1934, pp.213-5; *AJ*, LXXXII, 7 November 1935, pp.690-1.

Town Hall and Municipal Library, Wallington, Surrey (–1935). For Beddington and Wallington Urban District Council. The proposed layout plan is dated December 1933. Atkinson was appointed on the nomination of

Town Hall, Wallington, 1933

Sir Raymond Unwin, PRIBA; he knew the area well as it was not far from his former home at Carshalton. The Council offices were grouped round three sides of a square, in the centre of which stood the Council Chamber. The Library was housed in a separate single-storeyed building at the back, across a formal garden. (It was enlarged with an additional floor in 1962–3 by Robert Atkinson & Partners, who also built the adjacent Court House.) Beneath the central copper clocktower and pantiled roof, the building is of variegated red and brownish-red brick with fluted stone dresssings and features. The simplicity of these, and innovations such as the curved corners leading to the great stone portal at the rear, set it refreshingly apart from its neo-Georgian municipal contemporaries and approximate it in some degree, according to Pevsner, to the 'romanticism of Sweden and Holland in the 1920s'. Pevsner also believed the design to be 'decidedly pretty... though if compared say with Dudok's work at Hilversum, very minor and still very traditional' (*The Buildings of England, Surrey*). In 1979–80, the interior was refurbished and converted for use as courtrooms. See *A&BN*, CXLIV, 4 October 1935, pp.7-12; *BR*, CXLVI, 18 May 1934, pp.842-3; *AI*, VIII, April 1934, pp.108-13; *idem*, XI, October 1935, pp.123-31; *A&BN*, CXLVII, 18 September 1936, pp.342-5; *Building Design*, no.504, 11 July 1980, p.7. RA 1934 (1382).

1934 Dome Hall of Music and the Corn Exchange, Brighton. Additions and alterations for the County Borough of Brighton (–1935). See pp.34-5 of this publication; *AI*, VIII, April 1934, pp.114-19 and XII, January 1936, pp.1 and 13-19; *A&BN*, CXLI, 1935, 11 January, pp.65-69; *idem*, 18 January, supplement; *Some Notes on the Reconstructed Dome, supplied by the Architect, Mr Robert Atkinson,*

Broadwalk Court, London, 1934

1935; H. D. Roberts, *Souvenir of the Reconstructed Dome and Corn Exchange*, Lewes, 1937.

Broadwalk Court, Palace Gardens Terrace, Notting Hill Gate, London (–1935). For Sir Lindsay Parkinson and Co. Ltd. This was Atkinson's first block of flats. It comprises 100 apartments in eight storeys and an attic, built on a steel frame. The exterior is faced in variegated brick dressed with stone (mostly artificial) and, on the ground floor, faience. See *BR*, CXLVIII, 10 May 1935, pp. 879 and 881-2; *Building*, XI, February 1936, pp. 64 and 68. RA 1935 (1454).

Town Hall, Hackney. Unsuccessful competition entry (the commission went to Lanchester and Lodge). See *A&BN*, CXXXVII, 9 March 1934, pp. 314-18; *BR*, CXLVI, 16 March 1934, pp. 464-5. RA 1934 (1380).

Roedean Crescent, East Brighton. Proposed house for N. J. Hulbert.

Proposed hotel, Blackpool. For Sir Lindsay Parkinson & Co. Ltd. Atkinson quarrelled with the client and the project was abandoned. An unsuccessful legal action on Atkinson's part followed. See *A&BN*, CXLV, 27 March 1936, p. 387; *idem*, CXLVI, 3 April 1936, pp. 15-17; *AI*, XII, May 1936, pp. 141-9.

1935 'The White House' (Albany Court), Albany Street, Regent's Park, London (–1936). For Sir Lindsay Parkinson & Co. Ltd. See p. 36 of this publication; *A&BN*, CXLII, 10 May 1935, p. 147; *idem*, CXLVI, 26 June 1936, pp. 361-7 and supplement.; *BR*, CXLVIII, 10 May 1935, pp. 880 and 882; *idem*, CLI, 17 July 1936, pp. 108-11 and 117; *AR*, LXXX, 1936, pp. 71-2; *Building Design*, no. 340, 25 March 1977, p. 10. RA 1935 (1422).

Regency Lodge, Swiss Cottage, London (–1937). The site is an island at the junction of Adelaide, Avenue and Finchley Roads. Planning consent for the erection of a block of flats, shops and an underground garage was given in July 1935. The block consists of nine sections arranged round a central rectangular court with fountains. In all there are 107 flats. The exterior is of brownish and sand-coloured brick with artificial stone dressings. Tall vertical windows run up through four storeys to light the staircases. These were designed to save as much space as possible – there are no entrance halls as such. To east and west the blocks recede in step-like progression. On the west, the ground floor contains shops while on the east side there are bas-reliefs representing the various trades employed on the building. The underground garage provides parking for 100 cars. In *The Buildings of England, London*, 11, Pevsner described Regency Lodge as 'good, though a trifle stodgy'. See *A&BN*, CLIV, 15 April 1938, pp. 60-2; *AI*, XXII, September 1943, pp. 103-10; *BR*, CLXVII, 18 August 1944, pp. 125-9.

Barber Institute of Fine Arts, University of Birmingham (–1939). For the Trustees of the Barber Institute. On the building of the Barber Institute, see the essay on pp. 62-77 of this publication. See also *A&BN*, CXLV, 6 March 1936, p. 294; *Architectural Design and Construction*, VI, 8 June 1936, p. 254; *BR*, CLVI, 4 August 1939, pp. 195-8; *A&BN*, CLIX, 11 August 1939, pp. 155-9; *Building*, XIV, September 1939, pp. 382-4; *A&BN*, CXCII, 12 December 1947, p. 222. RA 1936 (1406).

1 Baker's Mews, Manchester Square, London. Internal alterations for Atkinson himself.

Regency Lodge, London, 1935

Cherkley Court, near Leatherhead, Surrey. New swimming pool, cinema and library for Lord Beaverbrook. See above (c.1920). See also *AI*, XI, September 1935, pp.69-70; *idem*, XII, October 1936, p.100-2 and November 1936, p.131.

1936 New Head Offices for the Gas Light & Coke Company, Horseferry Road, Westminster, London (not executed, though preparatory work on the site continued until 1940). Approval was given in principle in 1935 for the erection of a large new block of offices in a classicizing style on the site of the company's old headquarters and obsolete gas holders. The latter were demolished in 1935–6 and the old offices in 1937 but Atkinson's design was never built as the site was requisitioned for government purposes at the beginning of the War, and the company established its new chief office at Kensington Church Street. In 1949 Atkinson designed government offices for the same site; see below. See also *AJ*, XCV, 14 May 1942, pp.344 and 346; *BR*, CLXII, 8 May 1942, p.404; S. Everard, *The History of the Gas Light & Coke Company, 1812–1949*, 1949, pp.353-4. RA 1942 (740).

Oslo Court, Prince Albert Road, Regent's Park, London (–1937). See p.37 of this publication; *BR*, CLIV, 15 April 1938, pp.739-42; *A&BN*, CLIV, 20 May 1938, pp.212-15; *AR*, LXXXIII, June 1938, pp.278-81.

Stockleigh Hall, Prince Albert Road, Regent's Park, London (–1937). Atkinson collaborated with his partner, Anderson, on the design. A five-storey block of fifty flats on the site of an older building of the same name. The flats are grouped in six units around an open court which faces the park; each one has a direct view from at least one of its rooms. The external facing is soft-red brick with stone dressings – cf. Regency Lodge (1935–7) and Oslo Court (1936–7) – and the main ground floor frontages are

Stockleigh Hall, London, 1936

faced with artificial stone. The entrance lobbies are paved and lined with travertine marble, while the canopies over them are in reinforced concrete covered with copper. Stockleigh Hall was awarded the RIBA Bronze Medal for the best London building erected in 1937. Together with Oslo Court, it formed part of a development of large blocks of flats for the affluent in Portland Town to the north of Regent's Park. The development was more consistently in the modern style than any other in London. See *AI*, XII, April 1936, pp. 118-23; *AJ*, 7 May 1936, p. 693; *AR*, LXXXIII, June 1938, pp. 282-3; *A&BN*, CLIV, 20 May 1938, pp. 199 and 210-11. RA 1936 (1365).

Kensal House, Ladbroke Grove, North Kensington, London (–1937). For the Capitol Housing Association Ltd. This was a development of three blocks of workmen's flats and a nursery school for the employees of the Gas Light & Coke Company. The executant architect was Maxwell Fry, who produced the designs in collaboration with a committee comprising Atkinson, Elizabeth Denby, C. H. James and Grey Wornum. The site lies near the junction of Ladbroke Grove and Harrow Road, between the railway and the canal, and was previously part of the Kensal Green Gasworks. As a workers' colony, the flats may be compared with earlier schemes by Gropius and Le Corbusier. See *AR*, LXXXI, May 1937, pp. 207-10; S. Everard, *The History of the Gas Light & Coke Company, 1812–1949*, 1949, p. 352; (Various authors) *Flats*, Ascot Water Heaters Ltd, 1938, pp. 56-71; M. Fry, *Autobiographical Sketches*, 1975, pp. 143-4.

Proposed Film Studios, Elstree, Hertfordshire.

Butter Market, Sincil Street, Lincoln. This project formed part of Atkinson's proposals as town planning consultant to the Corporation of Lincoln. It involved rebuilding the front of the existing market.

Firlands Cottage, Burgess Hill, Sussex. Proposed alterations and additions.

Chalton Drive, Hampstead Garden Suburb, London. Proposed house for Mr M. Tanchan on a site at the corner of Chalton Drive and Norrice Lea.

178-180 Edgware Road, London. Offices and Showrooms for the Gas Light & Coke Company (–1938; demolished). See p.38 of this publication; *AI*, XV, December 1937, pp.159-61; *A&BN*, CLIII, 1938, 11 February, pp.187-9; *idem*, 18 February, supplement.

1937 Mickleham Downs House, near Leatherhead, Surrey. Alterations for Lord Beaverbrook.

Fire Station, Wallington, Surrey (–1938). For Beddington and Wallington Urban District Council. Atkinson worked in association with S. F. R. Carter, the Borough Engineer and Surveyor. The building is of brick with stone dressings and stands at the junction of Belmont and Bridge Roads, a short distance to the north of the Town Hall and Municipal Library (1933–5; see above). Over the door to the engine house is a coat-of-arms and lettering by W. Aumonier & Sons. See *A&BN*, CLIV, 29 April 1938, pp.117-19.

Town Hall, Acton, London (–1939). For the Borough of Acton. The executant architect of the building was W. G. Cross, the Borough Enginer, assisted by W. Leicester; Atkinson acted as consultant. The new building incorporated the old municipal offices and is in a sympathetic

style, making use of similar materials – red brick and Portland stone. Hope Bagenal advised on the acoustics. See *BR*, CLVII, 7 July 1939, pp.23-27.

24 and 25 Sussex Square and 9 Bathurst Street, Bayswater, London. Proposed rebuilding.

White Gate Cottage, Long Crendon, Buckinghamshire. Proposed alterations and additions for Judge Dale.

1938 Sir Henry Lunn's Travel Agency, 56 Haymarket, London (demolished). See p.39 of this publication; *A&BN*, CLIII, 11 February 1938, p.190; *AI*, XXII, March 1943, p.25.

Designs for street banners for the opening of the City Hall, Norwich. Atkinson was one of the assessors in the competition for the City Hall (built 1932–8 by C. H. James and S. R. Pierce and widely regarded as one of the foremost inter-war English public buildings). In 1936, he also designed the layout of the Market Place, since altered.

Electricity Showrooms and Offices, Wellesley Road, Croydon (–1939). For the County Borough of Croydon. The site is at the junction of Wellesley Road and Dingwall Avenue. Atkinson collaborated with his partner, Anderson, on the design. Three main blocks of brick with stone dressings are grouped round a central courtyard, connected by a semicircular closed arcade. The main wings are four-storeyed and faced with Portland stone. The third wing, of two floors only, was left in carcase, to be completed and extended upwards at

Butter Market, Lincoln, 1936

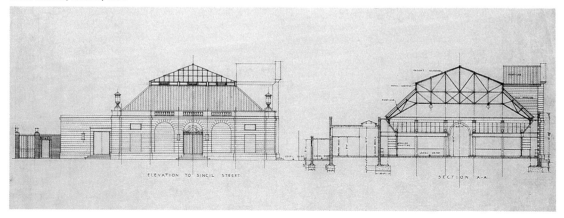

ELEVATION TO SINCIL STREET

SECTION A-A

a later date; it contains a lecture hall. Across the court-yard is the general showroom, and next to it, set on the diagonal at the corner of the building, the triangular entrance hall; above this, on the first floor, is a waiting room and an elliptical boardroom. The rest of the first floor contains offices, as do the second and third floors. Internally, the main entrance is of black marble and in the showrooms the walls are panelled in veneered walnut and black glass. Certain modifications to the original design were necessary because of the outbreak of war; for example the bronze for the window frames was made paper-thin and applied on hardwood cores. The stone urns on the roof of the arcade were a favourite motif of Atkinson's, according to C. H. Reilly in *Representative British Architects*. See *AI*, XXII, February 1943, pp. 13-24; *BR*, CLXV, 31 December 1943, pp. 528-32.

Petty Sessional Courts, Hatfield (–1939). The building is set back from the St Alban's Road and is of red (Chesham) brick with Portland stone dressings. It has a pantiled roof, with a copper-faced turret and weather vane. The parapet is ornamented with urns. Its style is close to that of Wallington Town Hall (1933–5; see above). See also *A&BN*, CLX, 27 October 1939, pp. 82-4.

All Hallows' Church, Chertsey Road, Twickenham (–1940). For the Diocese of London. The church was built with funds secured by the sale of the site of Wren's church of the same name, which stood off Lombard Street in the City of London. (This had developed subsidence cracks and was demolished, amidst much controversy, in 1938.) Atkinson won the commission at competition; one of the conditions was that the fittings of the old church, including the reredos, organ, font, pulpit and choirstalls, should be preserved in the new. The foundation stone was laid on 11 July 1939 and the church was consecrated on 9 November 1940. The tower of the old church was rebuilt and forms the entrance to the new building via a covered way which contains the monuments from the old church. The building is of orange-coloured brick, with Portland stone dressings and a buff pantile roof. Within, its arched windows and coffered roof evoke the original church, although this was much more ornamented. Hope Bagenal collaborated with Atkinson on the acoustics. See *BR*, CLIX, 13 December 1940, pp. 572-5; *AI*, XXII, July 1942, pp. 72 and 80-5; *CL*, CX, 2 November 1951, pp. 1464-5. For the controversy surrounding the demolition of the old church, see R. Byron, *How We Celebrate the Coronation*, 1937, reprinted in *AR*, LXXXI, May 1937, pp. 219-20.

Juniper Hill House, Mickleham, Surrey. Alterations which included modernization of the bedroom floors, reconditioning of the ground floor and the complete replanning of the basement, with the installation of a cinema. Hope Bagenal advised on the acoustics. The house dates from about 1780. See *AI*, XXII, December 1943, pp. 140-150.

Canadian Red Cross Hospital, Taplow, near Maidenhead, Berkshire (–1940). For the Canadian Red Cross Society. The building was erected from funds subscribed in Canada to the requirements of the Canadian Royal Army Medical Corps. The closing date for the submission of plans was the end of December 1939 and the hospital was handed over as operational on 16 July 1940. It consists of a central administration block, fronted by a large open portico, bearing the arms of Canada. Beyond this lay fifteen single-storey ward blocks, an officers' wing and medical, surgical, dental and other departments. In all, there was accommodation for 627 patients. Almost all the buildings are single-storey, built with a hollow wall of brick and terracotta slab, and roofed with steel trusses, covered with asbestos sheeting. From War Office drawings at the offices of Syborn & Atkinson, it seems likely that the design was based on officially recommended standard accommodation and that Anderson had a major hand in the project. These buildings are no longer operational as a hospital and may shortly be demolished by the National Trust. See *AI*, XXII, October 1942, pp. 115-25; *BR*, CLXIV, 15 January 1943, pp. 62-7.

c.1940 Design for a memorial to Percy Webster. Webster was a major figure in clock-making and restoration in the early decades of the century. He had premises in Great Portland Street and may have known Atkinson through the latter's interest in antiques. Atkinson's design is in the form of a Tuscan column with a cartouche bearing an inscription.

1941 Design for a clocktower. This may be in some way connected with the above project, though it is on a vastly greater scale.

1942 ARP Film Studios, Ealing. Extension (–1946) to the original building (–1929; see above).

1945 St Francis, Isleworth, Middlesex. Proposed internal alterations to a church built by E. C. Shearman (1933–5).

Croydon 'B' Power Station, Waddon Marsh, Croydon (–1951). For the British Electricity Authority. Atkinson was consultant architect to the civil engineers, C. S. Allott &

Juniper Hill House, Mickleham, 1938

Son, for whom he produced the general designs. The building, noted for its fine brickwork, is no longer in commission as a power sstation and is to be converted into flats and a shopping centre.

1946 Government Rehousing Scheme, Grand Parade, Gibraltar (–1950). For the Crown Agents for the Colonies. Atkinson and his partner, Anderson, collaborated on this large-scale project with a team of consultants under the general direction of R. W. Foxlee, Chief Civil Engineer of the Crown Agents. At the end of the War, there was an urgent need for housing in Gibraltar to accommodate returning evacuees, many of whom had new families. The site – chosen after considerable investigations – was south of the old city, in Governor's Meadow and Alameda Gardens. Here it was proposed to rehouse 3,000 people in 730 flats. Eventually 473 flats were erected, divided into seven blocks of an average of five

floors; five, known as Type 'A' blocks, stand on Governor's Meadow, next to the sea. Each block contains about sixty flats, planned round an internal courtyard. On the Lower Alameda Gardens site, two further blocks were built, known as 'M' and 'L' Types, different in design and slightly larger in scale than the Type 'A' Blocks. Three blocks proposed for the Upper Gardens were abandoned because of strong public disapproval. The buildings are steel-framed and, because of delays in bringing steel from England, it was mid September 1947 before a start was made on erecting the first block. The exterior facings are in yellow and brown plaster, with artificial stone dressings. Although most of the materials came from England, a point was made of using local materials where practicable, most obviously for the roofs, where 'Spanish tiles' were employed. A local building style was also attempted: open loggias or balconies were provided

57

for each family, as well as playgrounds for children and roof gardens for adults. Because of the restricted area of the site and the need for speed, as many of the structural parts as possible were prefabricated. For this reason, a full-size flat of identical materials was erected in England so that the details could be worked out in advance. Some shops and kiosks were built near the flats and the surrounding area was laid out by Clifford Holliday. See *BR*, CLXX, 1 March 1946, pp. 210-14; *Architectural Design and Construction*, XVI, May 1946, pp. 137-9; *BR*, CLXXIII, 26 September 1947, pp. 345-6; *idem*, CLXXVI, 14 January 1949, pp. 67-70.

8 King Street, St James's, London. Rebuilding for Christie, Manson & Woods Ltd (–1953). Atkinson drew up at least two schemes for the rebuilding of Christie's following war damage. Finally, however, it was decided to reconstruct the building as closely as possible to its former design – a commission which was largely carried out by Robert Atkinson & Partners after the death of Atkinson himself. (See also under Spencer House; below.)

1947 Spencer House, St James's Place, London. Interior alterations for Christie, Manson & Woods Ltd. Christie's offices and salerooms were at Spencer House from 1947 until 1953, while their bombed premises at 8 King Street were being rebuilt. (See also preceding entry.)

Proposed films studios. For Gaumont British Industrial Films Ltd.

Forty Avenue Flats, Wembley (–1949). For Wembley Borough Council. The site lies between Corringham Road and Barn Rise and contains five blocks, each of twelve low-cost flats. The blocks are of brick, with tiled roofs and buff facings. See *BR*, CLXXVII, 2 December 1949, pp. 733-6.

Westwood General Power Station, Ince-in-Makerfield, near Wigan (–1951). For the British Electricity Authority. Atkinson was consultant architect to the civil engineers, C. S. Allott & Son. The building is no longer in commission as a power station. See *Financial Times*, 2 August 1951, p. 6 (article by Trystan Edwards).

1948 Bridgewater House, St James's, London. External additions and internal alterations for the British Oxygen Company (–1949). Following war damage, Atkinson converted the building, originally by Charles Barry, into offices – 'exemplarily' according to Pevsner, in *The Buldings of England, London*, I.

Ratings' Quarters ('Edinburgh House'), Gibraltar (–1949). For the Admiralty. RA 1953 (1092).

Westwood General Power Station, Ince-in-Makerfield, 1947

1949 Cinema, Reclamation Road, Gibraltar (–1950). For the Royal Naval Trust. Built next to the Ratings' Quarters (see above), it had two Mainhill aeroplane hangars as its structural framework. See *Building*, XXVII, March 1951, pp. 100-5.

Vestry, Anglican Cathedral, Gibraltar (–1950). For the Diocese of Gibraltar. A two-storey addition to the Moorish-style cathedral of the Holy Trinity (1825–30). Atkinson also made designs for a porch and tower and for new north and south doors, but none was executed. See *Building*, XXVII, March 1952, pp. 90-2.

Parkmore Studios, Olympia Avenue, Johannesburg (–1950). For Africa Film Productions Ltd. The work was handled principally by Anderson, the studio specialist, and designs were sent to South Africa on a consultant basis.

Abinger House, Brighton. Rebuilding for Messrs Edlins

(–1954). Atkinson produced several designs for this public house to stand on the site of a nineteenth-century building damaged during the War, but he died before the commission was executed. See AR, CXVI, July 1954, p.50. RA 1954 (1167).

Government Offices, 2 Marsham Street, Westminster, London (–1971). For the Ministry of Works. The site runs along Marsham Street from its junction with Horseferry Road as far as Great Peter Street: part of it was intended for the new Head Offices of the Gas Light & Coke Company until its requisition by the government in 1940. The post-war history of this and adjacent sites is complicated. In 1949, Atkinson designed a vast office building for the Ministry of Housing and Local Government and the Department of Education and Science. Four perspectives by Cyril Farey show a monolithic neo-classical palace with five pairs of lateral wings running at right angles to the main north-south axis – and a megalomaniac scale that is shared with its successor, the present building on the site. The scheme was redesigned several times but Atkinson died before any decision had been taken on it. In the early 1960s, Eric Bedford, Chief Architect to the Ministry of Works, was called in and his ideas were the predominant influence thenceforth. Construction, which began in 1964, was supervised by Robert Atkinson & Partners. After much delay, the building opened in 1971 when, ironically, it became the home of the newly created Department of the Environment. See Building Design, no.624, 14 January 1983, p.1 (on the present building).

Army Barracks, Gibraltar.

Lorraine House, Manor Road, Wallington. Three blocks of flats for a site at the junction of Manor Road and Acre Lane (–1950).

St John's Church, Smith Square, Westminster, London. Proposed conversion to an ecclesiastical records office (–1951).

1950 Colman Galleries, Castle Museum, Norwich (–1951). For Norwich City Council. In 1943, R. J. Colman gave to the City of Norwich his collection of Norwich School pictures, together with a sum of money for the provision of new galleries to house it. Among those entrusted by the Council with the care of the pictures and the future building of the galleries at the Castle Museum was C. D. Medley, Atkinson's friend and Chairman of the Trustees of the Barber Institute. Atkinson was appointed architect of the project when Norwich was chosen as one of the four centres in England for special 1951 Festival of Britain activities and the building of the Colman Galleries was made a permanent part of the Festival plans. He was a logical choice, for the success of the Barber Institute was widely recognized and, only four years before, it had been awarded a RIBA Bronze Medal. Atkinson worked in association with the Norwich firm of Edward Boardman & Son, designing two galleries. These

Government Offices, Marsham Street, London, 1949

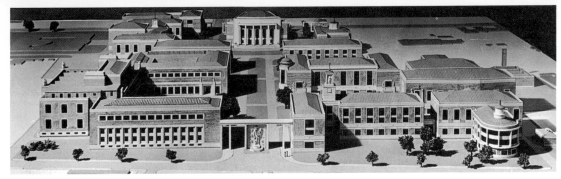

University buildings, Cambridge, 1952

are sited between the three main ones already in existence, in former garden recesses, whose awkward shapes he put to imaginative use. A large gallery with an apse was provided for the oil-paintings of J. S. Cotman and his followers, with a circulating gallery at one end for watercolours; the second gallery, intended for works by John Crome and other artists, consists of a main room surrounded by a series of variously shaped smaller ones, designed to have an intimate effect. His interiors reflect what he had learned at the Barber Institute in a number of ways, avoiding where possible right-angled corners, and setting sliding, rather than hinged, doors in the middle of walls. The system of lighting, however, is different, depending on broad lay-lights set in the central areas of the ceilings and surrounded by wide, shallow coving. By this method, it was intended to shade the wall space above the pictures and bring the natural light onto them. The height of the lay-lights was calculated to give domestic proportions to the rooms and to keep the source of light as low as necessary. (In these respects the system approximates to that used in the prints and drawings cabinets of the Barber Institute.) The galleries are heated through the floor by panel heating, augmented by air-conditioning. They were opened in June 1951. See *Building*, XXVII, June 1952, pp. 204-8; *Illustrated Guide to the Collection of Norwich School Pictures*, Norwich Castle Museum, June 1951, pp. 3-4 and 15-16.

Gloucester House, 13 Castlegate, York. Flats for the 1951 York Festival Society (–1951). York was designated a centre for the Festival of Britain and the three-storey block of flats was planned as an exhibit. The aim, as the City Engineer and Architect stated, was to 'show in a modern building that we are endeavouring to maintain the tradition of fine buildings in York'. Atkinson was one of three architects approached by the Festival Society – the others were Charles Holden and C. H. James. He acted as consulting architect, supplying the design and drawings to the City Engineer's Department. The flats were opened by the Duchess of Gloucester in June 1951. Their main external feature is a monumental entrance, with a broken segmental pediment. RA 1953 (1132).

Southacre Flats, Latham Road, Cambridge (–1951). The original scheme was for the conversion of Southacre House and the erection of six blocks of flats; only the conversion and two blocks were executed. The house has since been demolished.

Graham Robertson Room and Students' Room, Fitzwilliam Museum, Cambridge (–1955). For the Syndics of the Fitzwilliam Museum. These rooms were built with £10,000 left in 1949 by W. Graham Robertson towards the cost of a room for the display and storage of drawings and water-colours. They were set over ground-floor rooms already in existence. The plans were approved in 1951, but work did not begin until 1953; after Atkinson's death. Construction was subsequently supervised by his partner, Anderson, and the rooms were opened in May 1955.

1951 Technical College and College of Art, Fairfield, Croydon (–1959). For Croydon Corporation. Plans were drawn up in 1951 but building did not begin until 1953 – after Atkinson's death, Anderson took over the project. At the time the building was the largest technical college in the South of England, even though Atkinson's original proposals had been reduced. Construction was of brick and Portland stone over steel framing; the results were described by Pevsner in *The Buildings of England, Surrey*, as 'large and depressingly conventional'. The connection of the firm, Robert Atkinson & Partners, with the area continued in the 1960s: it built the Fairfield Halls (1960–2) and the Law Courts (1968–9) on adjoining sites. RA 1953 (1110).

1952 Proposed University buildings, Sidgwick Avenue, Cambridge. For the University of Cambridge. The scheme was not adopted and the present buildings on the site – the Arts Faculty (Casson Conder & Partners, designed 1952) and the History Faculty Library (James Stirling, 1964–8) – bear no relation to those envisaged by Atkinson.

RAF Station, North Front, Gibraltar.

UNIDENTIFIED OR UNDATED WORKS

1907–12 Factory, Wood Green, Vauxhall, London. For Messrs Barratt & Co.

Works, Vauxhall.

1912–15 Cinema at Burton-on-Trent. For Associated Provincial Picture Houses Ltd.

Cinemas at Dublin and Liverpool and proposed cinemas at Kensington and Leeds. For Provincial Cinematographic Theatres Ltd.

Garages at Blackheath and Old Southgate.

Offices for the British School of Motoring.

St Margaret's Studios, Twickenham.

Domestic work at 38 Bryanston Square, London; 11 and 13 Lower Belgrave Street, London; 1 Wilton Place, London; Harrow; Ryde House, Isle of Wight.

1918–29 Cottage, Bosham, Sussex. Proposed alterations for Mrs Newbould.

Rose Farm, Osterley, Middlesex. For Mrs Sills.

Concrete house. Design for the Red Triangle Cement Company. See F. R. Yerbury, *Small Modern English Houses*, 1929, pls. IX and X.

'Beechwaye', Gerrard's Cross, Buckinghamshire. For Mrs H. E. Campbell.

1930–35 The Square, Fernhurst, Sussex. Exterior and interior alterations.

Undated

Newington House, Oxfordshire (before 1924).

Cricket Court, Cricket Malherbie, Ilminster, Somerset. Alterations for Lord Beaverbrook.

House at West Kingston, Wiltshire.

Croydon 'B' Power Station, 1945

William Walcot, perspective of the Barber Institute, 1938

THE BARBER INSTITUTE OF FINE ARTS
University of Birmingham (1935–9)

Paul Spencer-Longhurst

In October 1932, the University of Birmingham was first made aware of the wish of Lady Barber to provide resources for a building on its Edgbaston site for the study of art and music. The prospective benefactress and her late husband, Sir (William) Henry Barber, Baronet (1860–1927), had long-standing connections with the city and University, and, during Sir Henry's lifetime, had apparently discussed a commemorative legacy of considerable size to further the arts in the University. Having no children, it was perhaps inevitable that they should have considered making charitable use of their fortune, accrued through property interests, in the city whence it had sprung. Encouraged by her friends, Sir Charles Grant Robertson (Vice-Chancellor) and Sir Gilbert Barling (Pro-Chancellor), Lady Barber let it be known that she hoped to set up a trust fund for the benefit in perpetuity of the

University.[1] From its accumulated income an Institute of Fine Arts was to be erected and equipped 'on land provided for that purpose by the University... to serve both as an art gallery or museum and a music room'.

Such was the essence of the proposal made to the University; once it had been approved by Council, a deed of settlement was drawn up to give it effect. Dated 13 December 1932, this was signed by Lady Barber and three newly appointed Life Trustees, including her solicitor, her banker and the Vice-Chancellor. It provided for the setting up of the envisaged trust fund in memory of Sir Henry, for the endowment of certain professorships, scholarships and prizes within the University and for the provision and maintenance of 'a building containing a music room and an art gallery or museum'. Four months later, Lady Barber herself died and the residue of her estate — reputed to have been not far short of £1,000,000 — went to augment the trust.

The receipt of this large sum allowed the Barber Trustees to proceed with plans for building the Institute early in 1934.[2] They first applied themselves to the question of finding a suitable architect, mainly, it seems, by relying on the contacts of their Chairman, Mr C. D. Medley.[3] It was he who chose Robert Atkinson, whom he knew mainly through his position as solicitor to the Architectural Association. Both men sat on the Council of the AA — Medley was elected an Honorary Member in 1933 — and on the permanent committee set up to deal with the award of Leverhulme scholarships. Both also belonged to the Arts Club, whose Dover Street premises often served as a meeting place for them during the building of the Institute.

Atkinson was not an immediately obvious choice as architect for the projected building. His expertise then mainly lay in the fields of cinema building and domestic work, and he had no practical experience in the design of museums or art galleries. He had drawn perspectives of the proposed new museum at Bolton for T. H. Mawson's book, *Bolton: A Study in Town Planning and Civic Art*, but that had been over twenty years before, and his only other venture into the field of gallery design had been his (unsuccessful) submissions to the 1911 competition for the proposed new art gallery and library at Manchester. Nevertheless, he was in his prime as an architect in the 1930s. He was recognized as the designer of the controversial 'jazz' entrance hall to the internationally renowned Daily Express Building and his public buildings were widely admired for their practicality as much as their aesthetic merit. He furthermore enjoyed a very high reputation in academic circles on account of his reform of the Architectural Association Schools and the publication in collaboration with Hope Bagenal of his *Theory and Elements of Architecture* in 1926. In addition to these qualities, Medley would have been aware of Atkinson's reputation as a collector. His office as well as his house was stocked with antique furniture, architectural books and works of art and he listed his interests in *Who's Who* as gardening and collecting. After his death his collection of pictures was sold at Christie's[4] and Howard Robertson observed that 'his collection of antiques was selective and choice; and his knowledge of architectural books a challenge to any bibliophile.'[5] From 1928 until 1940 a selection of twenty-five candlesticks and eight tapersticks from his collection of about two hundred, dating

1 For further details of the lives of Sir Henry and Lady Barber and of the circumstances of the establishment of the Barber Trust, see H. A. D. Miles, *Art in the University: The Early History of the Barber Institute* (text of inaugural lecture), University of Birmingham, 1972; and P. Spencer-Longhurst, *An Exhibition to Mark the Jubilee of the Barber Institute* (catalogue of the exhibition held at the Barber Institute), University of Birmingham, May–July 1983.

2 Minutes of their meeting held on 24 March that year record that they had met the University Site Committee.

3 Charles Douglas Medley Hon. LL D (Birmingham) (1870–1963), formerly solicitor to Lady Barber, was Senior Partner in the firm of Field Roscoe & Co., Lincoln's Inn Fields, and Chairman of the Guardian Assurance Co. Ltd. He remained Chairman of the Barber Trustees from his appointment until his death, but he lived in London and was well established there on the fringes of literary and intellectual circles.

4 31 July 1953, lot nos. 22–51.

5 *RIBAJ*, LX, January 1953, p.117.

from 1500 to 1750, was on loan to the Victoria and Albert Museum.[6] Such an architect could reasonably be assumed to have good ideas about the housing and display of works of art.

Atkinson was, moreover, stylistically conservative enough to be acceptable in a provincial milieu, an important consideration at a time when the Modern Movement, championed (mainly in London) by Behrens, Gropius, Breuer, Mendelsohn, Lubetkin and other refugees from Continental Europe, was establishing itself controversially as the new architecture. His most 'Modern' pre-war building, the White House, was still in the future and his thinking, as demonstrated by his work and teaching, stressed the importance of an awareness of and respect for historical style and local conditions. Even so, he might have been a difficult choice to justify in a great city with a proud architectural tradition of its own had he not had the advantage of good claims to Midlands roots, having been brought up and educated in Nottingham, where he lived until the age of twenty-two. No less useful was his connection with the Birmingham architect, William T. Benslyn (1884–1947), who had been his assistant from 1913 until 1923, when he moved to Birmingham to take up an appointment as architect to the City Education Committee. During the early part of his career, Atkinson had, moreover, built cinemas in the region – at Wolverhampton, Walsall, Wednesbury, Willenhall and Burton-on-Trent – and in 1927 had been an assessor in the competition for the Shakespeare Memorial Theatre at Stratford-upon-Avon.

Atkinson's appointment was duly announced in August 1934, the local press describing him as a 'famous architect'.[7] On 23 November, at a meeting of the Guild of Graduates of the University, the Pro-Chancellor, Sir Gilbert Barling, confirmed the site which had been allocated to the Institute.[8] It comprised about two acres opposite the newly built Union Building (by Holland W. Hobbiss, begun 1930), at the corner of Edgbaston Park Road and University Road. The site was chosen because it was both prominent, commanding one of the main entrances to the University, and relatively distant from the existing complex, allowing the new building to be erected in an independent style of architecture.[9] A large area was assigned because the University wanted the Institute 'to have a beautiful garden, and possibly fountains'; and because it was felt that the building was bound to grow.[10] An initial site-survey was carried out by the Birmingham architect, J. B. Surman.

At the time of his appointment, Atkinson was working on three major projects – Wallington Town Hall, the restoration of the Dome and Corn Exchange in Brighton and his first block of London flats, Broadwalk Court. He lost no time, however, in visiting the site and producing preliminary sketch plans of his brief.[11] By late December 1934 three different versions were already in existence. Of these the one designated Scheme 'A' showed an essentially square building, with corridors and ranges of rooms grouped around a central auditorium, which ran up through two storeys. Its orientation was north-south, the main entrance being at the south-east corner, facing the Union Building. The entrance was a major feature: set at forty-five degrees to the main axes of the building, it was almost an independent

6 Information kindly supplied by Miranda Poliakoff of the Metalwork Department.

7 See the *Birmingham Mail*, 17 August 1934; *Birmingham Post*, and *Birmingham Gazette*, 18 August 1934.

8 According to the minutes of the Trustees' meeting held on 18 October 1934, Atkinson himself preferred the site to others.

9 Report of the Pro- Chancellor's statement in the *Birmingham Post*, 24 November.

10 *Idem*.

11 No written brief as such survives – there may never have been one.

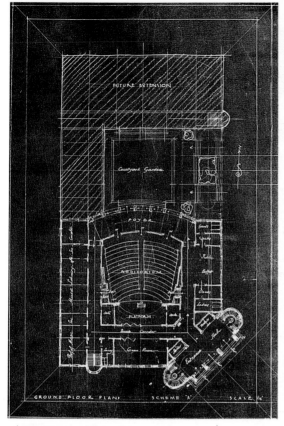

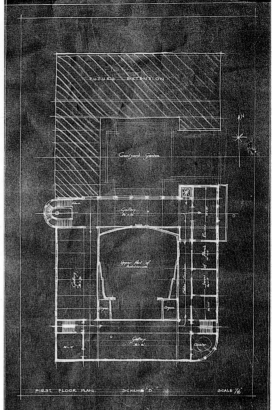

scheme 'A', ground-floor plan

scheme 'B', first-floor plan

12 Atkinson first used a corner entrance on a diagonal axis in his unexecuted competition design for the Usher Hall, Edinburgh (1910); this, too, had apsidal staircases at both ends, though it did not project from the main lines of the building. A contemporary comparison with the Barber Institute,

pavilion. Its rounded ends contained staircases leading up to a sculpture gallery.[12] On the ground floor, the accommodation was given over almost entirely to music and included a concert hall, a large green room, a public buffet and music library. Above, in addition to the sculpture gallery, there were two rectangular galleries measuring fifty-five by thirty feet; a curved gallery (above the foyer) of eighty by twenty feet; and, running along the west side, a series of 'period rooms' and an exhibition corridor ten feet wide. To the north was envisaged a square courtyard garden with a pool, and beyond it on two sides an L-shaped space, to be given over to a future extension.

Scheme 'B' (of which only the first-floor plan survives) was a much more recognizable relation of what actually came to be built. It retained the courtyard and

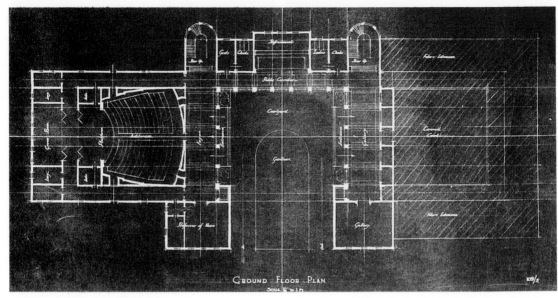

preliminary sketch plan of the ground floor

provision for a future extension, but moved the main entrance to the north-east corner and integrated it with the main axes of the building. There was only one principal staircase, which was placed in the north-west corner (the present position) and linked to the entrance by a straightened foyer. Its apsidal shape was retained and indeed reinforced by the rounding of the diagonally opposite south-east corner.[13] On the first floor, three rectangular galleries were provided – two of them enlarged at the expense of the now-abandoned sculpture gallery. Slightly altered in shape and size, the period rooms were translated to the east flank of the building, along with the exhibition corridor.

A third plan, later in numerical sequence, but probably representing the architect's first ideas, showed a building almost twice as large in area and consisting of

Scheme A, is provided by the Electricity Showrooms and Offices, Croydon (1938–9), where an oval boardroom is set over the corner entrance hall.

13 Apsidal stairways were much favoured by Atkinson in domestic settings, e.g., at Undertown, Trebetherick (1928–9).

66

three wings around a central court.[14] The auditorium lay through a foyer in the south wing and was entirely separate from the galleries, which were contained on the ground and first floors of the north wing. The west wing was given over to a refreshment room, cloakrooms and a public corridor on the ground floor, and, upstairs, to curatorial and secretarial accommodation. Despite the overall greater size of the building projected, the space allowed for the auditorium was almost identical to that in Schemes A and B and the gallery space was considerably smaller. This may have prompted Atkinson to make provision for a three-wing future extension, surrounding a covered court.

Thus matters stood when the University appointed the first Barber Professor of Fine Arts and Director of the Barber Institute, Thomas Bodkin.[15] A lawyer by training, Bodkin was Director of the National Gallery of Ireland before coming to Birmingham. Among his many qualities was a thorough knowledge of contemporary museum buildings and current gallery practice, acquired through extensive travel and wide reading while at Dublin. Only a few weeks, therefore, after his appointment and before officially taking up his duties, he wrote a long and detailed letter to the architect, giving his views, not all of them positive, on the plans for the Institute.[16] In this he expressed the opinion (shared by Medley) that Atkinson's Scheme B should be the basis on which to work, but indicated that less accommodation should be given to the performance of music, and more assigned to the teaching of art history. For this a lecture room, art library and photograph and slide libraries were needed; consequently, the music library would have to be reduced and a room provided for the storage and conservation of works of art. The foyer and corridors would have to be cut down in size and the green room and buffet eliminated. Bodkin then proceeded to comment on the proposed galleries in the following terms:

> My chief objection to the plans for the galleries is against the system of lighting proposed. The spectator would stand between the light and the pictures on the walls in all the galleries, looking, therefore, either at his own shadow or reflection. I think it absolutely essential that the galleries should be top-lit, and would strongly recommend the system used in the new rooms at the Fitzwilliam Museum in Cambridge. I have seen most of the recently built picture galleries on the Continent and consider that the Fitzwilliam is as good as or better than any of them.[17] Moreover, provision of suitable top-lighting would almost double the area of wall space available for the display of pictures, tapestries, or other works of art.
>
> I do not like the entries to the various galleries being placed in an angle. People using the galleries as a thoroughfare would tend to walk between the spectators and the exhibits. If the galleries were entered by doors in the middle of the shorter walls a much better general effect and idea of their contents would be gained immediately.
>
> As there will be, it is hoped, a steady and continuous growth in the collections of pictures and other objects of art, the provision of as much wall space as possible is desirous, and if wedge-shaped bays were arranged

14 Drawing no.109/5. Schemes A and B seem to have been numbered retrospectively.

15 Thomas Patrick Bodkin, KSG, MRIA, Hon. D.Litt. and LLD (National University of Ireland), Hon. Litt.D. (Dublin); Barrister-at-Law (1887–1961). His appointment to Birmingham was made on 5 December 1934 and he assumed office on 1 March 1935.

16 Letter dated 26 January 1935. All letters cited are at the Barber Institute unless otherwise indicated.

17 The 'new rooms' at the Fitzwilliam were the Courtauld Galleries by Smith & Brewer, opened in 1931. They were lit by the new Seager method of indirect daylight.

67

along the walls the area available for the display of pictures would be nearly doubled.[18] The interior of such wedges affords a very useful storing accommodation. I would like to see at least the east and west galleries so arranged. 'Period rooms' have not proved as a rule satisfactory or popular. They take up more space than they are worth as it is difficult to use their right-angled corners for exhibition purposes. Moreover, with only three or four such rooms it would be a very invidious task to decide what special periods should be represented therein.

Most of Bodkin's points were taken by Atkinson as he clarified his ideas. The new Director's intervention had the immediate effect of defining the function of the building as primarily that of an art gallery rather than a concert hall.[19] Atkinson also responded to Bodkin's reference to the excellence of the new galleries at the Fitzwilliam Museum, which he visited in the company of Medley in mid February and recorded in measured plans. By early April the definitive layout of the Institute was in existence. It was a development of Scheme B, consisting of a concert room or music auditorium in the centre, surrounded by corridors and departmental accommodation on the ground floor and galleries on the floor above. The only major modification to the ground plan was the rounding of the south-west corner and the extension of the six central bays of the south front into a round-cornered projection, which was to provide more accommodation for a lecture theatre on the ground floor and a reserve gallery above. This is shown clearly on a north-south section of about the same date, which also demonstrates the careful attention being paid to the lighting of the galleries and the projection facilities in the music auditorium and lecture theatre.[20] In the latter connection, Atkinson's experience as a designer of cinemas must have been extremely useful.

From the beginning, Atkinson envisaged an impressive building. His initial idea was to face it with Portland stone up to first-floor level. Above that brick would be used – not 'the fierce red brick already used on the University building (1900–9, by Aston Webb and Ingress Bell), but something more harmonious'.[21] Drawings made in May 1935 show a frieze of artists' names running round the parapet of the Institute, figurative sculpture on both ground and first floors, and busts over the french windows of the north front; also a formal garden with loggia, ornamental pool and a curious standard of enormous height to the right of the building.[22] The sculpture and names were quickly eliminated but two other aspects of the design gave rise to some discussion. The first was the proposed stone facing of the lower storey, which the Vice-Chancellor initially objected to on the grounds that it would clash with the unrelieved brick of the Union and other buildings. The second was the aesthetic effect of the construction, then imminent, of the King Edward's Schools on the site across the Edgbaston Park Road.[23] Atkinson undertook to consult their architect, Holland Hobbiss, 'with an idea of collaborating to some extent'.[24]

In August, Atkinson reported to Bodkin that he was proceeding rapidly with his drawings and the two men planned a tour that autumn of Germany, Holland, Belgium and France in order to inspect the best European examples of recent

18 This method of display was in use at the National Portrait Gallery, London, where space was limited, then as now.
19 Medley and the Vice-Chancellor supported the new Director in this. Grant Robertson reiterated 'the fact that music is quite subsidiary to the fine arts in the founder's scheme'. Perhaps in the knowledge of the architect's reputation as a designer of cinemas he continued, 'The Institute is not to be, in any sense, a place of public entertainment' (quoted in Bodkin's letter of 26 January, see note 16 above).
20 Drawing no.109/10J.
21 Letter to Bodkin, dated 18 May 1935.
22 Drawing nos.109/11F and 109/12F.
23 King Edward VI Grammar School and King Edward VI High School for Girls were begun in 1937 and opened in 1940. They are built in variegated red brick, the boys' school in an essentially neo-Georgian style with some Tudor references, the girls' school displaying more classical detail.
24 The only evidence of such possible collaboration appears in the harmonizing colours of the buildings' brickwork and Atkinson's use of dark header patterning on the upper storey of the Barber Institute. There are, however, precedents for diaper and other vernacular patterning in his earlier work, e.g., at Preston Grange (1914–18).

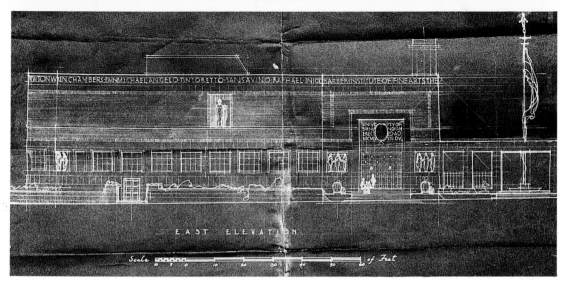

EAST ELEVATION

Scale of Feet

elevation of east facade, May 1935

ground-floor plan as built

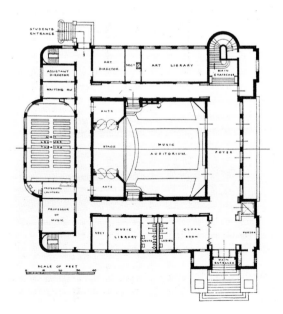

first-floor plan as built

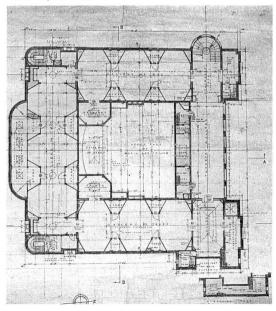

museum architecture.[25] A direct result of this visit was a drawing comparing the structure and lighting systems of galleries in the Gemeentemuseum at The Hague, the Boymans Museum in Rotterdam and the Fitzwilliam Museum.[26] With this drawing Atkinson sent a diagram indicating the lighting of a typical gallery in the Institute and a diagrammatic internal perspective showing its intended effect.[27] From these it is evident that he sought to combine the best features of the Fitzwilliam and the Boymans Museums in his own suggestions. A letter accompanying his drawings stated that his aim was 'to get a good-looking gallery, rather than one which looks as though it were full of gadgets' and that he had made everything 'as simple and as straightforward' as he could.[28] The proposed wall coverings of light-coloured, coarse-weave hessian and the system of suspending pictures on rods from rails were both influenced by what Atkinson and Bodkin had seen together in Holland.

By mid October the plans for the exterior of the Institute were complete and had been approved by the Trustees and the University authorities. Plans for the interior remained 'not yet fully worked out'.[29] By the end of November, however, they were sufficiently advanced to be revealed to senior members of the University and local notables at a conversazione for 1,100 guests.[30]

Drawings survive dating from the first few days of November which were almost certainly among those exhibited at the conversazione.[31] They show a building about 120 feet square. On the first floor the picture galleries are arranged in a square around the upper part of the music auditorium. Galleries One, Two and Three are single top-lit halls opening into one another and each punctuated by three pairs of facing bays. From One and Three open smaller rooms for the display of drawings and prints respectively, and from Two there is access to space for the Reserve Collection. Beyond Three is a small gallery, about thirty feet by fifteen feet, which leads back through the Tapestry Gallery to the main staircase hall. To one side of this, opposite Gallery One, opens a photographic studio.[32] Below, the academic accommodation is similarly arranged around the music auditorium at the centre. It includes rooms for the Director, his Assistant and Secretary and the Music Professor; art and music libraries and a lecture theatre. The lower ground floor contains music rehearsal rooms, part of the art library, the caretaker's flat, a service kitchen and general storage and service space.

Mid December witnessed the issuing of the invitation to tender for the building and two months later a contract was signed with a Birmingham firm, Maddocks and Walford. The final estimate of the total cost exceeded the sum set aside under the terms of the trust deed by about twenty-five per cent but was eventually approved as much of the excess was accountable to unforeseen problems with the foundations. The site had been previously used as a gravel pit and afterwards filled in with the rubble from some of the University buildings, so that excavations had to be made to a depth of about fifteen feet. The Portland stone proposed for the facing of the lower storeys was replaced at the final moment, on grounds of cost and availability, by Darley Dale stone, which was complemented at the upper levels by handmade Himley brick.

25 The tour was undertaken in late September and early October and included visits to the Kunsthalle, Hamburg, the Rijksmuseum, Amsterdam, the Gemeentemuseum at The Hague, the Boymans Museum, Rotterdam, and the Palais des Beaux-Arts at Brussels. The following year, in April 1936, they visited the new rooms for Asiatic sculpture (not yet open to the public) at the Louvre, and the Jeu de Paume in order to see their new systems of artificial lighting. Of these contemporary classics of gallery design, the Boymans Museum (A. van der Steur, 1931–5) and the Gemeente-museum at The Hague (H. P. Berlage, 1930–5) were featured at this time in the *Architect and Building News*, CXLIII, 1935, 13 September, pp. 296-301, 20 September, pp. 330-6, 27 September, pp. 355-9. Bodkin also drew Atkinson's attention to a newly published work on museum and gallery design, *Muséographie*, (2 vols., Office Internationale des Musées, Paris, 1934).

26 Drawing no. 109/15/1.

27 Drawing nos. 109/14/F and 109/16/B respectively.

28 Letter dated 24 October 1935.

29 T. Bodkin, *The Place of the Fine Arts in the University* (text of inaugural lecture), University of Birmingham, 1935, p. 23.

30 Held on 29 November in the Aston Webb Building.

31 Drawing nos. 109/21/J, 109/23/J and 109/24/J.

32 The studio now acts as a lobby to the new Reserve.

Cyril Farey, perspective of the Barber Institute, 1936

33 It is shown in an elevation of May 1935 (109/11/F).

34 George Atkinson, RHA, ARCA (1880–1941), Headmaster of the Dublin Metropolitan School of Art, was a leading Irish printmaker and letterer.

35 Gordon Herickx (1900–53) had been a pupil at the Birmingham College of Art and in the early 1930s turned to producing sculptures in the manner of Gaudier-Brzeska and

For the design of the inscription over the entrance, conceived from an early stage as an essential feature,[33] Bodkin proposed an Irish sculptor, George Atkinson (no relation) whom he believed to be 'even better than Eric Gill for the particular job'.[34] The design was made in the form of templates and confided for execution to a local man, Gordon Herickx, of Birmingham Sculptors, Moseley,[35] who also executed the heraldic shields on either side of the entrance and the other external adornments. In place of the original scheme's figurative sculpture, the architect proposed urns, a favourite motif of his, to stand in four niches on the upper storey at the south-east and south-west corners.[36] In practice, however, these proved unsatisfactory, owing to the height and comparative shallowness of the niches, so they were replaced by large stone slabs, carved in bold relief, with a branch of laurel, a palm

71

leaf, a lyre and a torch to symbolize the Fine Arts, the Reward of Merit, Music and Education respectively.[37]

The general construction of the building is in brick, with steel beams to carry the floors, which are of reinforced concrete. By mid November 1936, the basement was complete and work had begun on the ground floor. A mere seven months later the Institute had reached cornice level and by August the twin turrets on the north elevation were in place. Shortly afterwards, Bodkin was able to report that 'everybody in Birmingham now seems to be pleased with it'.[38] Meanwhile, with the support of Atkinson, he had been actively pursuing in Dublin the acquisition of an eighteenth-century bronze monumental statue of King George I for the gardens in front of the Institute.[39] In October Atkinson set about designing a plinth for the statue, remarking characteristically that 'it would look very well in the middle of the semicircular approach, and would give us a very fine kick as a start off'.[40] Thus, directly in the angle of vision from the University's East Gate is one of the finest Baroque sculptures in the country, leading the eye on to the twentieth-century lines of the building itself.[41]

Most of the exterior construction was complete by the end of 1937. Building work during 1938 concentrated on the interior – in both its practical and aesthetic aspects. A major consideration was the heating and ventilation, a subject which had been discussed at length between Atkinson, the consulting engineers Messrs Cramp & Frith, and the contractors, Richard Crittall & Co. The main argument hinged on whether a plenum system envisaged for the picture galleries should be augmented by a system of humidity control. Enquiries were made concerning the systems used at the National Gallery, the Tate Gallery and the Fitzwilliam Museum, and it was discovered that those institutions had given up attempts at humidity control based on separate refrigeration units. It was therefore decided to limit the air-conditioning at the Institute to what could be achieved by the adjustment of the plenum system to outside weather conditions. This installation was crucial to the conservation of pictures and Atkinson's long experience in the heating and ventilation of large spaces by means of forced air was of great value – particularly that gained at his cinemas, where temperature and humidity were liable to dramatic change.[42] For the rest of the building, and as an extra in the galleries, heating was by radiator panels set in the concrete of the ceilings.

The lighting of the three main galleries was by individual rooflights over the bays, which admitted daylight in such a way as to prevent reflection from the glass covering the pictures. Natural light could be supplemented by artificial means, or lowered by the drawing of blinds below the rooflights. For the fourth gallery, which was to display Lady Barber's collection of tapestries, Atkinson created a side-lit room without bays. Opposite the windows he installed oak panelling as a background for the tapestries – a statement of the unique function of the room, which, with its small display of furniture, had more of a 'country house' atmosphere than the other galleries. In the decoration of the galleries, elaborate ornament and strong colours were ruled out, so as not to distract from any work of art; instead, the walls were covered in a discreet oatmeal hessian. Fittings for the prints and

Brancusi. His partners at Birmingham Sculptors were Bernard Mason and Frank Bullows.

36 'Fine urns . . . are almost his trademark', commented C. H. Reilly (loc.cit., p.39). A contemporary instance of their use is the arcade of the Electricity Showrooms and Offices, Croydon (1938–9).

37 Director's Report, Barber Institute, University of Birmingham, 1937, pp.1-2. The idea was Bodkin's.

38 Letter to Atkinson, dated 28 September 1937.

39 Attributed to the Anglo-Flemish sculptor, John van Nost the Elder (active 1686, died 1729). The sculpture had been set up on Essex Bridge, Dublin in 1722 and transferred to the garden of the Mansion House after 1753. By 1928 it had been taken down in anticipation of disposal. After lengthy negotiations, Bodkin secured it for the Barber Institute from the Corporation of Dublin at a cost of £500.

40 Letter to Bodkin, dated 28 May 1937.

41 Atkinson's first idea was to set the sculpture on a tall, plain plinth, on an axis at right angles to the front of the building. Situated at its left corner, directly before the basement door, it was no doubt intended to balance the monumental entrance at the right. He changed this, however, moving the statue further to the left, setting it at an angle to the Institute and reducing the height of the plinth to about ten feet. It originally stood at the junction of the three wide stone pathways, one of which led back to the basement door. This layout was altered at the

gallery one
music auditorium

drawings cabinets, including a special locking display rail, were based on those in the recently opened Charrington Print Room at the Fitzwilliam.

Throughout the building the quality of materials was consistently high: travertine for the floor of the foyer, the staircase and the architraves of the doors in the galleries; light oak for the dados and parquet floors of the galleries and other internal woodwork. Downstairs, things were more functional, but retained a certain elegance. Here the floors were covered in rubber linoleum – still *in situ* – whose pale green rectilinear patterns complemented the shallow coffering of the ceilings above. For the lecture theatre and art and music libraries, furniture was commissioned from Gordon Russell, while Atkinson himself designed a lectern and even a hatstand for the service stairs.

The music auditorium, which seats 364 people, is panelled in Australian walnut, while the proscenium and stage are in much lighter satin inlaid maple. In this room more than anywhere else – apart, perhaps, from the patterned brickwork over the main entrance – Atkinson's colour sense and tendency to a decorative style are evident. Around the top of the panelling in the auditorium runs a series of crescent festoons, inlaid in light on dark, and suggesting loops of curtaining. The slight hint of classical ornament which they also give is continued on the sides of the proscenium by angular motifs reminiscent of the Greek key pattern. Along the soffit of the proscenium runs an interlocking pattern of curves and right angles – of which a variant is repeated vertically on the main doors. The stepped ceiling is divided into a series of diminishing shallow coffered squares painted buff, white, grey-blue and cream. In his planning of the auditorium, Atkinson obviously benefited from his recent experience in the interior rebuilding of the Dome Hall of Music, Brighton (1934–5). He also consulted the Professor of Music, Victor Hely-Hutchinson, on the proportions and layout, and was advised on the acoustics by Hope Bagenal.

The Institute was opened on 26 July 1939 by Queen Mary.[43] At that time, in addition to the collection of tapestries, English furniture, lace and needlework formerly owned by Lady Barber, the Trust had acquired sixteen paintings, thirty-one drawings and water-colours, nineteen prints, three sculptures, six pieces of furniture and applied art and three finely printed books. There was little chance to display this small collection, however, as the War supervened almost immediately. Only a month after the opening the basement had been taken over as a first-aid station and, indeed, seemed to suit this sudden change of role so well that Bodkin reported to Atkinson that the medical authorities had said it was as good 'for that purpose as if you had designed it *ad hoc*'.[44]

From its opening the building was widely praised, both for its aesthetic and functional merits. The Trustees were delighted with it and specially commissioned a perspective from William Walcot. Bodkin, who had formed a deep respect for Atkinson from the start, was fulsome in his praise:

Mr Atkinson had to face a complicated and unprecedented problem. The site provided was ample but awkward, a triangular space bounded on two sides by main roads converging into a narrow point. Existing University buildings

time of the construction of the University Ring Road in 1963.
42 A major example was the Regent Cinema, Brighton, where 100,000 cubic feet of warm air was forced into the building per minute.
43 At her suggestion a small bronze rail was added to the front of the platform in the lecture theatre.
44 Letter dated 4 September 1939.

73

in close proximity precluded the possibility of designing a structure that should be strikingly divergent from them in style or noticeably different in material. The accommodation that was called for necessitated intricate planning: exhibition galleries, a room for recitals of chamber music, a lecture theatre, art and music libraries and their appurtenant stack rooms, offices, practice rooms, waiting rooms, cloakrooms, workshops, storage and living quarters for the resident attendant, had all to be fitted within the same shell, which, in view of its destined purpose, should be in itself a manifest work of art. In the resultant building, all these exacting demands have been triumphantly met.[45]

The intervening half-century has done nothing to diminish enthusiasm for the building, both on the part of those who use it daily, and those who visit it from near and far. At the time of Atkinson's death *The Times* declared 'this admirable building' to be 'the purest example' of his work.[46] In 1981 it was listed Grade II, and four years later, Sir John Summerson stated that it represented 'better than almost any other building (except, perhaps, the RIBA in Portland Place) the spirit of English architecture in the 1930s.'[47]

Summerson analysed the style of the building and related it to its function of '... combining ... an art gallery and a post-graduate school of art history. This was a new type of institution, inviting fresh architectural ideas ... Atkinson's unusual plan, with the auditorium locked into a square of galleries, the projecting lecture theatre and off-centre entrance, put conventional Classicism out of the question. Atkinson adopted a kind of Anglo-Swedish classic, allowing complete freedom of movement while retaining traditional elements and the use of traditional building materials.'[48] The listed building description speaks of 'a sophisticated design, marrying elements of traditional institutional Classicism with Dudok-inspired stone-dressed brick modern'.[49] The combination of stone and subtly variegated brickwork sets the building firmly in its period and also in an international context, linking it with, for example, Asplund's Public Library, Stockholm (1920–8), Dudok's Hilversum Town Hall (1926–8) and Van der Steur's Boymans Museum, Rotterdam (1931–5). Its shape and materials give hints of housing projects of the 1920s and 1930s in Germany and Holland, such as Häring's farm at Gut Garkau, near Lübeck (1924), or Oud's housing estate at Hook of Holland (1926–7). Specific influences from such sources – apart from the museums which Atkinson visited with Bodkin – are difficult to trace, but there is plenty of evidence for his interest in contemporary Northern European architecture from his period as Principal and Director of Education at the Architectural Association. During his tenure of office visits were undertaken to Holland (1922), Sweden (1925) and Germany (1929) and lectures were given by architects from those countries, notably A. Keppler (1922), H. Wijdeveld and H. Ahlberg (1924) and W. Hegemann (1928).[50] In his own teaching Atkinson also set great store by the Beaux-Arts and American architectural traditions and we should not be surprised to see quotations from classical French architecture at the Barber Institute. Two such instances are the use of shallow recessed panels à la Mansart on the corners of the building, and the abandoned row of busts above

45 Reported in *Builder*, CLVII, 4 August 1939, p.195.
46 Obituary, 29 December 1952.
47 J. Summerson, 'The Architecture of British Museums and Art Galleries', in J. Chapel and C. Gere, eds., *The Fine and Decorative Art Collections of Britain and Ireland*, NACF/Weidenfeld & Nicolson, 1985, p.18.
48 *Idem*.
49 Cited in L. Braithwaite, *Architectural Trail*, University of Birmingham, 1987, p.25.
50 J. Summerson, *The Architectural Association, 1847–1947*, London, 1947, p.45.

Barber Institute in 1939

51 Concerning the scale and
monumentality of the entrance,
it should be recalled that from
the beginning, a future
extension to the right,
balancing the present facade
to the left, was planned –
indeed, such a scheme was
not finally abandoned until
the 1960s. The scale and
proportions of the entrance
are echoed on the other side
of the University Campus at

the french windows on the north front, distantly recalling the *cour d'honneur* at Versailles.

Yet at the same time, The Barber Institute is conceived within the British architectural vernacular of its day, eschewing a too overt Classicism or any self-assertive posturing in favour of an expression without of the function within. The most obvious examples of this are the monumental entrance, leading to the foyer with its spacious proportions and almost Baroque side-lit vista, and the blind upper storey which emphasizes the presence behind it of top-lit galleries.[51] Among British forebears the name of Soane comes to mind, particularly if the stripped classical pilasters and other interior features of the building are considered. In particular, the turrets surmounting the north facade with their fluted capital-less pilasters and projecting shallow entablatures recall Soane's work at Dulwich Picture Gallery (1811–14), as does Atkinson's unclassical use of a Doric frieze of alternating triglyphs and metopes along the parapet of the Institute.[52]

To speak of the Barber Institute as a work of art in its own right is no exaggeration. Each detail is satisfying in itself yet combines with others to produce a whole, of which the keynote is balance. This is particularly noticeable on the front elevation, which is dominated by its raised portico-like entrance, once compared with an Egyptian pylon.[53] It is surmounted by a 'jazz' aureole of herringbone brickwork, which could easily have stolen the entire effect, had not Atkinson had the sensitivity to connect it with the rest of the facade and emphasize its horizontal elements with a narrow stone string course. At the other end of the facade a vertical counterweight to the porch is provided by the carved stone slab which rests on the string course at the second bay and unites it with the stone coping above. The verticality of this bay is increased by the basement entrance below and, less obviously, by the variation of the motif of the frieze above. This motif, derived from the Greek key pattern but very much 1930s in style, exemplifies another essential feature of the building – namely unity. For its squared angles are not only repeated along the parapet over each of the inset stone slabs, but are found also – rotated through ninety degrees – in the metalwork of the main inner doors. The design on these main doors is in turn closely related to the inlay of the music auditorium doors and, turned back to the horizontal, to that on the soffit of the proscenium. An equally striking, though now vanished, instance of the wholeness of Atkinson's design was the ornamental semicircular layout of the paving at the bottom of the main steps, which was in a herringbone design to complement the brickwork over the entrance. Sadly this was destroyed when the North Ring Road was constructed in the early 1960s.

In general, however, the Barber Institute has survived the passing of half a century remarkably well, with very few architectural or structural alterations. It narrowly escaped the bombs which fell on the campus at Easter 1941[54] and the first major change was the addition in 1965–6 of the music library in the north-west corner – a single-storey building of brick and stone by Atkinson's successors, Robert Atkinson & Partners. (The siting of this was an admission that more grandiose plans for a large extension to the Institute with a formal garden had been abandoned.) In 1971 the same firm drew up plans for a new art library on the other side of the main staircase behind the building, but these came to nothing. Part of the Reserve Gallery on the south side was converted into a Coin Gallery in 1972–4 by the firm's successors, Syborn & Atkinson, who in 1974 also began a new reserve over the music library. Most recently major structural work, involving the construction of a new metal and glass roof, the rebuilding of the air-conditioning plant within it and the conversion of the Tapestry Gallery to a fourth top-lit gallery for the display of pictures was undertaken by Bickerdike Allen Partners. It is the completion of this work and the restoration of the building to normal conditions which is being celebrated this year – by happy coincidence, exactly fifty years after the opening of the Barber Institute in July 1939.

opposite:
staircase in entrance hall

the contemporary Medical School by Lanchester and Lodge and in the terrace entrance to Atkinson's Wallington Town Hall (1933–5).

52 Similar turrets first made their appearance in Atkinson's work in a drawing dated 1912 connected with his submission for the Port of London Authority Head Office competition (reproduced in *Academy Architecture*, XLVII, 1915, pp.44-5). At the Barber Institute the turrets originally served to cover a life shaft and water tank.

53 D. Hickman, *Birmingham*, Studio Vista/November Books, 1970, p.66.

54 See M. Cheesewright, *Mirror to a Mermaid*, University of Birmingham, 1975, p.99.

ROBERT ATKINSON 1883–1952
BIOGRAPHICAL NOTES

1883 Born 1 August at Wigton, near Carlisle, Cumberland, where his father was a cabinet-maker.

c.1890 Began education at Wigton School.

1896 Entered Nottingham School of Art as a part-time student (–1906), while working in an architect's office. Charles Gascoyne was a contemporary student.

1898 Articled to James Harris, Bridlesmith Gate, Nottingham.

1899 Articled to 'Mr Dyson', Newcastle. While in articles he designed and built a row of cottages (untraced), acting as his own contractor.

1900 Enrolled for one year as a day student at University College, Nottingham. Thereafter he continued his studies in the evenings both there and at the School of Art.

1904 Awarded the Dutton Walker Scholarship at Nottingham School of Art, which enabled him to spend one year there as a day student. Passed Final Examination in architecture. Won Silver and Bronze Medals in the National Competition of the Board of Education, South Kensington.

1905 Won two Silver Medals in the National Competition of the Board of Education and the Tite Prize of the RIBA. Came to London and worked as an assistant in the office of John Belcher – mainly on competition entries. Spent nine months travelling in Italy, France, Germany, Holland, Algeria and other countries.

1906 Awarded a Silver Medal for measured drawings of Italy in the National Competition of the Board of Education; and a book prize for studies of buildings. Awarded a Certificate of Honourable Mention (second prize) in the Soane Medallion Competition of the RIBA. Worked as a perspective draughtsman in the office of C. E. Mallows; began period of collaboration with R. Frank Atkinson (not a relation) and the leading landscape-architect, T. H. Mawson.

The major contemporary account of Atkinson's career is given in C. H. Reilly's *Representative British Architects of the Present Day* (published 1931, reprinted 1967), pp. 28-39. The most important accounts which appeared after his death are the following: Anon., obituary, *The Times*, 30 December 1952 and John Betjeman's addendum, *The Times*, 31 December 1952; *BR*, CLXXXIV, 2 January 1953, p. 21, obituary by Howard Robertson; *RIBAJ*, LX, January 1953, p. 117, obituaries by Howard Robertson and Neil Martin-Kaye; F. R. Yerbury, 'Robert Atkinson', *AAJ*, LXVIII, February 1953, pp. 118-21; Hope Bagenal, 'Robert Atkinson and the Theory of Architecture', *AAJ*, LXVIII, May 1953, pp. 201-3.

1907 Set up in practice at 2 South Square, Gray's Inn, with Charles Gascoyne, Alick Horsnell and George Nott.

1910 Elected ARIBA (28 February). His proposers were R. Frank Atkinson, Alfred W. S. Cross and C. E. Mallows.

1911 Moved his practice to 11 Old Queen Street, Westminster.

1912 Entered partnership with George Luard Alexander, a pupil of the church architect. G. F. Bodley. Moved office to 199 Piccadilly. Invited at the suggestion of Austin Hall, Secretary of the Architectural Association School of Architecture, to become Visiting Master in Design at the Evening School.

1913 Appointed Head Master (later known as Principal) of the Architectural Association School(–1920).

1915 Elected FRIBA (7 June). His proposers were Edwin Cooper, Henry V. Ashley and F. Winton Newman.

1917 Supervised the removal of the Architectural Association from Tufton Street to Bedford Square, where he redesigned the interiors.

1918 Took William T. Benslyn as his assistant and later partner, following the death in action of George Alexander. Moved his practice to offices adjoining the premises of the Architectural Association, at 35 and 36 Bedford Square.

1919 Visited the United States to report on American architectural education for the RIBA and study American cinema design.

1920 Resigned as Principal of the Architectural Association and took up the more advisory post of Director of Education (–1929).

1922 Atkinson's *Report on the Education of the Architect in the United States of America* published by the RIBA.

1924 Entered partnership at 126 Wigmore Street with Alexander Frederick Berenbruck Anderson (1888–1968), who held the Diploma of the Ecole des Beaux-Arts, Paris.

1926 Published, with Hope Bagenal, *Theory and Elements of Architecture*, vol.1, part 1, largely based on Atkinson's lectures at the Architectural Association. Further volumes, though intended, were never published, but each section was from the first envisaged as a 'complete and separate unit'.

1927 Awarded an honorary MA(Arch) by the University of Liverpool. Appointed an assessor of the competitions for the Shakespeare Memorial Theatre, Stratford-upon-Avon, and the extension to Manchester Town Hall and Public Library.

1929 Retired as Director of Education at the Architectural Association (succeeded by Howard Robertson).

1931 Member of the committee of assessors for the RIBA Building, Portland Place. Appointed assessor of the competition for the new City Hall, Norwich, and consultant architect to the City Council on the surrounding area. His *Norwich from a Stranger's Viewpoint* was published by the Norwich Publicity Assocation.

1932 Appointed a Director of the Building Centre.

1934 Atkinson and Anderson move their practice to 13 Manchester Square. Atkinson appointed consultant architect to the City Council of Lincoln to advise on planning.

1935 An assessor of the competition for County Hall, Hertford, and consultant to the Gas Light & Coke Co.

1937 With Anderson, awarded the RIBA London Architecture Bronze Medal for Stockleigh Hall, Regent's Park.

1945 Appointed consultant (with Anderson) by the Crown Agents for Government building projects in Gibraltar.

1946 Awarded the RIBA Architecture Bronze Medal for the Barber Institute by the Birmingham and Five Counties Architectural Association.

1951 OBE

1952 Died 26 December.

THE BARBER INSTITUTE EXHIBITION

The idea of an exhibition to celebrate the life and work of Robert Atkinson was prompted by the rebuilding which has taken place at the Barber Institute of Fine Arts at the University of Birmingham over the last three years. By a happy coincidence, its completion falls almost exactly fifty years after the opening of the building in July 1939, thus providing an appropriate occasion for honouring an architect who, though successful and renowned in his own day, has become unfairly obscure since his death – a fate shared by many of his generation. Atkinson's long connection with the Architectural Association makes it a particularly suitable London venue for the exhibition.

Valuable help and support in the planning and preparation of the exhibition has come from many quarters, for all of which the organizer is extremely grateful; especially that which was so readily forthcoming from the Trustees of the Barber Institute, its Director Professor H. A. D. Miles, and Alvin Boyarsky, Chairman of the Architectural Association. Special thanks are due to Gavin Stamp and Alan Powers for their major contributions to the planning of the exhibition and to its catalogue. The organizer has greatly benefited from the help and advice of past and present members of Atkinson's firm and its successors – the late John R. Atkinson, David Beaty-Pownall, Eric Garthside, Tony Rose, John Scott, Rosemary Stjernstedt and Victor and Philip Syborn. He also wishes to thank particularly John Bagenal, Patricia Brock, David Elwall, Cathy Mainstone, Norman Riley and Nicholas V. Thompson. Gavin Stamp would like to thank Jessica Rutherford and John Roles of the Royal Pavilion, Art Gallery and Museums in Brighton, Philip Way, Film and Photographic Officer of the Central Electricity Generating Board, South-Eastern Region, and Donald Finlay, of the Council for the Care of Churches.

The main archives of Atkinson drawings are in the British Architectural Library/RIBA Drawings Collection and with Messrs Syborn & Atkinson. A number of drawings from both sources have been kindly lent for the exhibition at the Architectural Association. The Barber Institute is prevented by its founding Deed of Settlement from displaying borrowed material in its galleries and the exhibition there takes the form of drawings and photographs from its own archives.

Paul Spencer-Longhurst

This publication has been produced to coincide with two consecutive exhibitions of the work of the architect Robert Atkinson held in Summer/Autumn 1989 at the Barber Institute of Fine Arts, University of Birmingham and the Architectural Association in London. The Barber Institute exhibition has been organized by Paul Spencer-Longhurst. The Architectural Association exhibition and the publication have been organized through the office of the Chairman, Alvin Boyarsky, assisted by Micki Hawkes. *Robert Atkinson 1883–1952* has been produced for AA Publications by Pamela Johnston (production editor) and Dennis Crompton (technical co-ordinator) with Annie Bridges, Dominique Murray, Stuart Smith, Marilyn Sparrow and Mark Vernon-Jones.

Photographs on the pages noted are reproduced with the permission of the: Architectural Press 33 bottom and centre left, right, 37; Trustees of the Barber Institute, University of Birmingham 62, 65, 66-7, 69, 73; British Architectural Library/RIBA 32, 36, 40, 41, 42, 43, 47, 48, 49, 50, 51; Central Electricity Generating Board 61; National Monuments Record 28 left, 44; Royal Pavilion, Art Gallery and Museums, Brighton 27, 35; Gavin Stamp 34; Syborn & Atkinson 22-3, 25 top, 26, 28 top, 29, 31 bottom, 38-9, 53, 57 (photographs by Dell and Wainwright), 52. The photographs on pages 14-15, 16, 18, 19, 20-1, 28 bottom right and 33 top left are from the F. R. Yerbury archive at the Architectural Association. Additional photography of material in the archive of Syborn & Atkinson by Geremy Butler.

Production services by Book Production Consultants, Cambridge
Printed and bound by Black Bear Press, Cambridge
ISBN 1 870890 16 7

673016